K12 Classics
for Young Readers

Volume C

Book Staff and Contributors

Kristen Kinney-Haines *Director, Primary Literacy*
Beth Zemble *Director, Alternative Learning Strategies, Director, English Language Arts*
Mary Beck Desmond *Senior Text Editor*
Karen Ingebretsen *Text Editor*
Suzanne Montazer *Creative Director, Print and ePublishing*
Jayoung Cho, Oltjen Design Associates *Print Visual Designers*
Kim Barcas, Stephanie Shaw Williams *Cover Designers*
Amy Eward *Senior Manager, Writers*
Susan Raley *Senior Manager, Editors*
Alden Davidson *Project Manager*

Maria Szalay *Executive Vice President, Product Development*
John Holdren *Senior Vice President, Content and Curriculum*
David Pelizzari *Vice President, Content and Curriculum*
Kim Barcas *Vice President, Creative*
Laura Seuschek *Vice President, Instructional Design, Evaluation & Studies*
Chris Frescholtz *Senior Director, Program Management*

Lisa Dimaio Iekel *Senior Production Manager*
Ray Traugott *Production Manager*

Illustrations Credits

All illustrations © K12 unless otherwise noted

Nicole Wong, 2–3; Sarolta Szulyovsky, 4–5; Ian Joven, 6–11; Wendy Rasmussen, 12–17; Micha Archer, 18–25; Robert Meganck, 26–31; Lael Henderson, 32 –41; Jenny Sylvaine, 42–51; Bandelin-Dacey Studios, 52–65; Mike Reed, 66–67; Dan Boris, 68–69; Judy Love, 70–73; Francesca Carabelli, 74–75; Wendy Rasmussen, 76–77; Colleen Madden, 78–85; Lael Henderson, 86–89; Robert Meganck, 90–93; Kristin Sorra, 94–113; Nicole Wong, 114–115; Chi Chung, 116–117; Jennifer Zivoin, 118–121; Carolina Farías, 122–125; Sarolta Szulyovsky, 126–133; Mike Bohman, 134–139; Yu-Mei Han, 140–151; Micha Archer, 152–177; Ivan Stalio, 178–187; Yevgenia Nayberg, 188–191; Mike Bohman, 192–199; Kristin Sorra, 200–203; Yu-Mei Han, 204–213; Yevgenia Nayberg, 214–219

About K12 Inc.

K12 Inc. (NYSE: LRN) drives innovation and advances the quality of education by delivering state-of-the-art digital learning platforms and technology to students and school districts around the world. K12 is a company of educators offering its online and blended curriculum to charter schools, public school districts, private schools, and directly to families. More information can be found at K12.com.

978-1-60153-305-0

Printed by Worzalla, Stevens Point, WI, USA, April, 2019

Contents

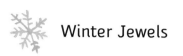 

K¹² Classics
for Young Readers

Volume C

The **Wind** and the **Sun**

adapted from a fable by Aesop

One day, the Wind and the Sun **exchanged** words about which was the stronger.

"I am the stronger," puffed the Wind. "See how I can send the black clouds flying through the sky."

"No doubt you are strong," was the Sun's gentle reply. "But how can you prove that you are stronger than I?"

"I can soon prove that," said the Wind. "You see that man walking along the road? Let us agree that he is the stronger who can make the man take off his coat."

"Agreed!" said the Sun. "You may try first."

So the Wind blew a **fierce** blast. It blew harder and harder. But the man only turned his back to the Wind and wrapped his coat more closely around him.

In vain, the noisy Wind tried to blow the man's coat off. Then the Wind said to the Sun, "It is your turn to try now."

So the Sun sent some gentle rays down upon the man. Soon the man became so warm that he was glad to unbutton his coat.

---

exchanged gave and received
fierce wild or scary
in vain without success

By and by, he became so warm that he pulled off his coat and hung it on his arm.

Thus, the gentle Sun proved that he was stronger than the noisy Wind. Gentle ways often **prevail** when **rough** ones fail. ❧

....

prevail to be successful; to overcome
rough forceful

The **Bundle** *of* **Sticks**

adapted from a fable by Aesop

There once was a man whose family argued **constantly**. He had tried in many ways to teach them not to **quarrel** but had failed.

One day, he called his sons together. He told them to lay a **bundle** of sticks before him. He tied a strong **cord** firmly around the bundle of sticks. He told his sons, one after the other, to take up the bundle and break it. They all tried, but they could not break the bundle.

Then the father untied the cord and gave his sons the sticks to break, one by one. They did this with the greatest ease.

Then the father said, "You are like the sticks, my sons. As long as you stand by each other, you are strong. You can do great things, meet any **challenge**, and stand up to any enemy. When you quarrel and separate, you are easily beaten. In **unity**, there is strength."

constantly without stopping

quarrel argue

bundle a group of things bound or tied together

cord woven or twisted thread

challenge a difficult task or problem

unity agreement on a purpose; being joined together as a whole

Why *the* Larks Flew Away

A family of four young **larks** once lived with their mother in a nest in a wheat field. At first, the nest was very safe, for it stood on the soft ground and was hidden by the wheat.

When the wheat began to **ripen**, the mother lark watched carefully for any sign of the coming of the **reapers**. She feared that the sharp knives would cut the nest and **injure** the young larks.

One morning, she had to leave the nest to find some breakfast for her little ones.

"Be good children and stay in the nest," she said. "If the farmer and his son pass through the field, listen very carefully to what they say."

"Yes, Mother," cried the four baby larks.

The mother lark flew away. A few minutes later, the little larks heard the farmer and his son passing along the narrow path near the nest.

---

larks a kind of songbird

ripen for a fruit or vegetable to become ready to pick

reapers people who cut ripe fruit or vegetables with a curved blade or a reaping machine

injure hurt

"This wheat is ripe enough to cut," said the farmer. "John, go down the road to Neighbor Smith's farmhouse and ask him to come tomorrow to help us reap the grain."

When the mother lark came home, she brought some fat worms for breakfast. She found her babies chirping excitedly.

"Mother! Mother!" they cried. "The men are coming to cut the wheat. We must move away tonight!"

"What did the farmer say?" asked the mother lark.

"The farmer told his son to go over to Neighbor Smith's house and ask him to help cut the grain."

"My dear children," laughed the mother lark, "as yet, we have nothing to fear."

When the baby larks had eaten their breakfast, the mother lark showed them how to exercise their wings.

The next morning, before leaving, the mother lark said once more, "Stay in the nest, and if the farmer passes through the field, listen to what he says."

"Yes, Mother," cried the little larks.

Away flew the mother, and again the farmer and his son passed through the fields.

"Did you ask Neighbor Smith to help us cut the grain?" **inquired** the farmer.

"Yes, Father," replied the son, "and I expected him here already."

"The wheat is ripe, and it should be cut without **delay**," replied the farmer. "**Mount** your horse and ride to your cousins' house. Ask them if they will help us."

This frightened the baby larks so much that when they saw their mother coming, they began to chirp more loudly than ever.

"What is the trouble?" called the mother as she **hastened** toward the nest.

"We must surely go away today!" cried the young larks. "The farmer's son has gone to bring his cousins to cut the wheat. We shall be killed if we stay here."

Again the mother laughed. "If the farmer waits for his cousins to help him, the wheat will not be cut today."

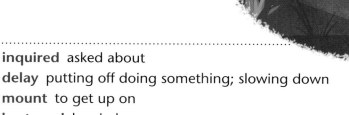

inquired asked about
delay putting off doing something; slowing down
mount to get up on
hastened hurried

WHY THE LARKS FLEW AWAY

The third morning, the mother left the nest to search for food. At noon, the farmer and his son came into the field.

"See how late it is," said the farmer, "and still not a man has come to help us. I see we must do the work ourselves. Let us go home and get everything ready. Tomorrow, before the sun is up, we shall begin to reap."

Soon after the farmer had gone, the mother lark came flying over the wheat field. The little larks told her all that they had heard.

"Now, indeed, it is time for us to be off," she said. "Shake your wings and get ready to fly. When a man makes up his mind to do his own work, it is sure to be done at once."

Chipmunk
and Bear

an Iroquois tale, retold by Joseph Bruchac

Long ago, when animals could talk, a bear was walking along. Now, it has always been said that bears think very highly of themselves. Since they are big and strong, they are certain that they are the most important of the animals.

As this bear went along, turning over big logs with his paws to look for food to eat, he felt very sure of himself. "There is nothing I cannot do," said the bear.

"Is that so?" said a small voice. Bear looked down. There was a little chipmunk looking up at the bear from its hole in the ground.

"Yes," Bear said, "that is true indeed." He reached out one huge paw and rolled over a big log. "Look at how easily I can do this. I am the strongest of all the animals. I can do anything. All the other animals fear me."

"Can you stop the sun from rising in the morning?" said Chipmunk.

Bear thought for a moment. "I have never tried that," he said. "Yes, I am sure I could stop the sun from rising."

"You are sure?" said Chipmunk.

"I am sure," said Bear. "Tomorrow morning, the sun will not rise. I, Bear, have said so." Bear sat down facing the east to wait.

Behind him, the sun set for the night, and still he sat there. Chipmunk went into his hole and curled up in his **snug** little nest, **chuckling** about how foolish Bear was. All through the night, Bear sat. Finally the first birds started their songs, and the east glowed with the light that comes before the sun.

"The sun will not rise today," said Bear. He stared hard at the growing light. "The sun will not rise today."

However, the sun rose, just as it always had. Bear was very upset, but Chipmunk was delighted. He laughed and laughed. "Sun is stronger than Bear," said Chipmunk, **twittering** with laughter. Chipmunk was so **amused** that he came out of his hole and began running around in circles, singing this song:

The sun came up,
The sun came up.
Bear is angry,
But the sun came up.

....

snug warm, close, and comfortable
chuckling laughing quietly
twittering making chirping noises
amused entertained

While Bear sat there looking very unhappy, Chipmunk ran around and around, singing and laughing until he was so weak that he rolled over on his back. Then quicker than the leap of a fish from a stream, Bear shot out one big paw and pinned Chipmunk to the ground.

"Perhaps I cannot stop the sun from rising," said Bear, "but you will never see another sunrise."

"Oh, Bear," said Chipmunk, "oh, oh, oh, you are the strongest, you are the quickest, you are the best of all the animals. I was only joking." But Bear did not move his paw.

"Oh, Bear," Chipmunk said, "you are right to kill me. I deserve to die. Just please let me say one last prayer to the Creator before you eat me."

"Say your prayer quickly," said Bear. "Your time to walk the Sky Road has come!"

"Oh, Bear," said Chipmunk, "I would like to die. But you are pressing down on me so hard that I cannot breathe. I can hardly squeak. I do not have enough breath to say a prayer. If you would just lift your paw a little, just a little bit, then I could breathe. And I could say my last prayer to the Maker of all, to the one who made great, wise, powerful Bear and foolish, weak, little Chipmunk."

Bear lifted up his paw. He lifted it just a little bit. That little bit, though, was enough. Chipmunk squirmed free and ran for his hole as quickly as the blinking of an eye. Bear swung his paw at the little chipmunk as he **darted** away, but the very tips of his long claws scraped along Chipmunk's back, leaving three pale scars.

To this day, all chipmunks wear those scars as a reminder to them of what happens when one animal makes fun of another. ᜁ

darted moved very quickly

The *Tiger,* the *Brahman,* and the *Jackal*

Once upon a time in India, a **Brahman** was walking along the road. His mind was so filled with calm thoughts that he hardly noticed where he was going.

As he walked along in peace, he was **startled** by the sound of a most **desperate** growling, roaring, and snapping of teeth.

He looked up to see a tiger caught in a large cage. The tiger was biting at the bars in **rage**, but **in vain**.

When the tiger saw the Brahman, he cried out, "My holy friend, please let me out of this trap."

The kind Brahman began to open the trap but then stopped. "No," he said, "for I fear that if I **release** you, you will eat me. After all, it is in your nature."

"It is in my nature to be free!" replied the tiger. "I promise, if you release me, I will do you no harm. I will serve you forever!"

Brahman a holy or wise person in Indian society
startled surprised
desperate having lost all hope
rage great anger
in vain without hope
release free; let go

"A Brahman has no need of a servant," said the holy man. "And besides, once you are out of this cage, you are likely to forget your promises."

The Brahman turned and began to walk away. But then the tiger called out in a pitiful voice, "Would you leave me here to die? Is that the way of a holy man?"

At this, the Brahman stopped. Then he turned back and opened the door of the cage. In one bound, the tiger popped out and grabbed the Brahman. "Thank you, my foolish friend," said the tiger. "And now, as I have been trapped for so long, and have grown very hungry, I must eat you!"

"Wait one minute!" cried the Brahman. "I gave you your freedom. Now give me a chance for mine. If I can find three things that say you should let me go free, then will you let me go?"

"I will," said the tiger, "but be quick about it. I am hungry!"

So the Brahman turned to a nearby tree and asked, "Oh, tree! You saw me let this tiger out of the trap. Is it not right that the tiger should let me go free?"

But the tree replied, "Why do you complain? Look at me. I give shade to all who pass by, and how do they thank me? They tear off my branches to feed to their animals. Take what is coming to you—be a man!"

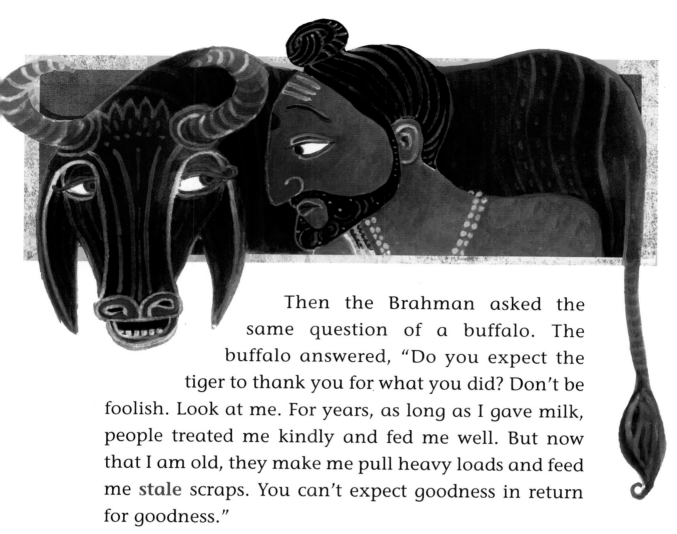

Then the Brahman asked the same question of a buffalo. The buffalo answered, "Do you expect the tiger to thank you for what you did? Don't be foolish. Look at me. For years, as long as I gave milk, people treated me kindly and fed me well. But now that I am old, they make me pull heavy loads and feed me **stale** scraps. You can't expect goodness in return for goodness."

The sad Brahman asked the road what he thought of the matter. The road answered, "My good sir, do you really expect thanks for your kindness? Look at me. All day long, people walk on me. And how do they thank me for this service? They spit on me and throw their trash on me."

"**Alas!**" cried the Brahman. "It appears I must be eaten."

-----

stale not fresh
alas oh, no

Just as the Brahman turned to face the hungry tiger, a **jackal** walked up. "Oh good and holy man," said the jackal, "why do you look so sad on such a fine day?"

The Brahman told him all that had happened. He told how he had found the tiger trapped in the cage. He told how he had let the tiger go free. He explained how he asked the tree, buffalo, and road for their opinions. "And now," he sadly concluded, "it appears I must be eaten."

The jackal scratched his head and said with a puzzled look, "Would you please tell me the story again? I'm afraid I found it very confusing."

Once more the Brahman told what had happened. When he finished, the jackal said, "I am sorry to be so **slow-witted**, but I'm afraid I still don't understand. Let me see—the tiger was walking along and found the Brahman in the cage . . . ."

"No!" roared the tiger. "Have you no brain at all? The Brahman was not in the cage. I was in the cage!"

"Oh, yes, of course," said the jackal. "I was in the cage and—oh, no, that's not quite right. Let me try again. The tiger was in the Brahman, and then the buffalo opened the tiger, and—oh, dear, I'm afraid I simply can't understand it!"

....

jackal a kind of a wild dog found in Africa and Asia
slow-witted not smart

"You will understand," growled the tiger. "Now listen carefully. I am the tiger. Do you see that?"

"Yes, my lord," said the jackal in a meek voice.

"And this man is the Brahman."

"Yes, my lord."

"And right here is the cage."

"Indeed, my lord."

"And I was in this cage— do you see?" said the tiger.

"Yes, my lord. I was—I mean, you were—I mean, the Brahman was—oh, dear, dear, just when it seems to make sense, I get all confused again!"

"What will it take to make you understand?" the tiger roared.

"Perhaps, my lord," said the jackal, "if we could start at the beginning, and if you would be so kind as to show me what happened. Now, the Brahman was in the cage . . . ."

"No!" shouted the tiger. "I was in the cage— like this!" He stepped inside the cage. "Now do you understand, you foolish jackal?"

"Indeed, my lord," said the jackal as he stepped forth and, with one quick movement, shut and locked the cage. "I understand perfectly!" ✖

Squirrel and Spider

Once Squirrel wanted to grow a crop of grain on his farm. He worked hard to get his farm in fine condition. He dug the soil, planted and watered the seeds, and pulled the weeds. Day after day he worked, and at night he went home to his tree to rest. Since Squirrel was very good at climbing trees, he did not need to make a road to his farm. Instead he traveled to and from his farm by jumping from one tree to another.

One day, when Squirrel's grain was almost ripe, Spider went out looking for food. Along the way, Spider came near Squirrel's farm. In the **distance**, he could see the tall grain waving in the breeze.

"What fine-looking fields," Spider thought **greedily**. "I would be very pleased to have fields like these, and all that grain for myself."

Spider searched for a road to the farm, but he could not find one since Squirrel reached the farm by jumping from tree to tree. Spider went home. He told his family all about the fine farm he had found. Then **cunning** Spider made a plan.

---

distance a faraway point or place
greedily selfishly
cunning tricky

The very next day, the whole Spider family started out early. Spider and his wife and children worked together all day to build a road to the farm.

When they finished making the road, Spider built his web across it. Then he threw pieces of clay pots along the path. He made it look like his children had dropped the pieces while working on the farm.

Spider's **trickery** made it look like the farm belonged to him. Now he and his family began to cut down Squirrel's good, ripe grain and carry it away.

Squirrel saw that someone was robbing his fields. At first he did not know who could be stealing his grain. He said to himself, "I will watch for the thief." So he hid in a tall tree nearby.

....
trickery use of tricks to cheat

SQUIRREL AND SPIDER

Soon enough, Spider came to the fields again to take more grain. Squirrel jumped out of his tree.

"What right do you have to take my grain?" Squirrel asked Spider. But Spider at once asked him the very same question.

"What right do you have to take *my* grain?" demanded Spider.

"These are my fields," said Squirrel.

"Oh, no! They are mine," replied Spider.

"I dug them and planted them and watered them and weeded them," said Squirrel.

"Then where is your road to them?" asked **crafty** Spider.

"I need no road. I travel by the trees," said Squirrel. Spider laughed at such an answer. He continued to use the farm as if it were his own.

....

crafty clever

Squirrel went to a judge to say whose farm it was.

The judge scratched his chin and thought. Then he said, "No one has ever had a farm without a road leading to it. So the land must belong to Spider."

Poor Squirrel tried to explain, but the judge would allow no argument. In much joy, Spider and his family gathered all the rest of the grain from the farm. They cut it and tied it in large bundles. Then they started for the nearest market to sell it.

When they were about halfway to the market, a storm overtook them. Spider and his family ran for **shelter**. But the winds were so strong that they could not carry their bundles with them. They had to leave the bundles of grain by the side of the road.

When the storm was over, Spider and his family returned to pick up their grain. As they **approached** the spot where they had left it, they saw a large black crow. His broad wings were **stretched** over the bundles to keep them dry. Spider approached Crow.

shelter safe cover
approached went toward
stretched spread out

"Thank you for so kindly taking care of my grain," said Spider. Then he tried to take the bundles.

"*Your* grain!" replied Crow. "Who ever heard of anyone leaving bundles of grain by the roadside? Nonsense! This grain is mine."

Then Crow picked up the bundles and flew off with them. Greedy Spider and his wife and children returned home sad and empty-handed.

Their stealing had done them no good. Someone had taken from them what they had taken from another.

Charlie and Topsy

Once there was a little boy named Charlie. He lived with his mother and daddy and auntie in a house in the city. A cat called Jane and Jane's kitten, whose name was Topsy, also lived in the house.

Charlie was a good boy and everybody liked him. Everybody, that is, except Jane the cat and Topsy the kitten. They did not like him at all.

This was very sad, because Charlie loved Jane and Topsy more than anything else in the world, except his mother, daddy, and auntie. He loved Jane and Topsy a thousand times more than his electric train set or even his **enormous** flashlight.

Yet Jane and Topsy ran away whenever they saw him coming. And what do you think was the reason?

The reason was this: Charlie liked that cat and kitten so much that he was never happy unless he was holding them tight in his arms and **squeezing** them all day long. Whenever he saw them running on their own four legs, he would grab them and squeeze them and bother them. Most of the time he grabbed Topsy, because the kitten was little and couldn't run away so fast.

....

enormous huge
squeezing pressing together too tightly from two sides

Again and again, his mother and auntie said to him, "Charlie, put that kitten down! Don't you see that he doesn't want to be held all the time? Let him run around and play. You wouldn't like it if we were to carry you around all day and hug you and squeeze you. Just run around and let him chase you. A kitten loves to run and **scamper** and jump, but he does not like to be picked up and carried all the time."

But Charlie would not listen. He picked the kitten up all the time, and he would not let him run around at all. He **bothered** and teased him all day long. Topsy called out, "Meow, meow," but Charlie paid no attention. He just went on squeezing and teasing the poor kitten.

....

scamper to run about playfully
bothered pestered

One day, Charlie was walking around in the yard looking for Topsy. Topsy was hiding in the bushes near the fence. He was hiding because he did not want to be grabbed and hugged and squeezed.

Charlie saw Topsy and reached out his hand to grab the kitten. But suddenly, a great big hand grabbed Charlie! Yes, a great big hand grabbed him by his **trousers** and lifted him clear off the ground and over the fence. And a great big voice called out, "Oooo-eee! What a darling little teeny-tiny creature!"

....

trousers pants

CHARLIE AND TOPSY

Charlie **squirmed** around to see what was holding him. It was a giant little girl. She had brown hair tied with a red bow, and all in all she was a very pretty girl—and very big, more than twice as big as Charlie's mother, daddy, or auntie.

She looked at Charlie and again she squealed, "Oooo-eee! You darling little thing! I'm going to take you home right this minute." She began to run, still holding Charlie by his trousers. She ran so fast that his head bobbed up and down.

Charlie called out, "Put me down! Put me down!" But the giant little girl paid no attention at all.

"Mama! Mama!" she cried. "Look what I found. It's a darling, teeny little doll. And it's alive, Mama! It walks and it talks!"

"That's nice, dear," said the girl's mama. "Take care not to tease it or drag it about."

But the girl paid no attention. She poked Charlie in the middle of his back and said, "Walk. Walk!"

"Ouch! Don't do that!" cried Charlie.

Then she lifted Charlie high in the air and kissed him and squeezed him and hugged him till Charlie thought he could not breathe. And he did not like it one bit.

....

squirmed twisted like a worm

The girl ran out of the room but came right back with an enormous piece of cake. She stuffed a piece into Charlie's face. "Look, Mama," she cried, "he can eat like a real live person. Isn't he cute? Do you want some more, little person?"

Charlie realized that he was in fact very hungry, so he reached for the cake. But the girl held it just out of his reach. When he jumped for it, she pulled it away and laughed.

"Mama," called the girl, "may I go over and show him to Sophie? Please, Mama, please?"

The girl's mama said she might go and show Charlie to Sophie, but she mustn't stay long. Charlie kicked and cried out, "I want to go home!" But the girl paid no attention. She picked him up and stuffed him in her pocket and started to run to show Sophie.

There were many things in the girl's pocket—pencils, a nail, and some sharp pebbles. As the girl ran, these things bumped and knocked poor Charlie.

But there was one more thing in the girl's pocket—a hole! The next thing Charlie knew, he fell through the hole and landed with a thump in the road. The girl ran on, and she never knew till she got to Sophie's house that she had lost Charlie through the hole in her pocket.

As for Charlie, you can guess how fast he ran! He ran and ran and never stopped till he got home. He rushed into the living room where his mother and auntie were sitting. Jane and Topsy were there as well. When they saw Charlie, they **scurried** behind the bookcase.

"Oh, Mother! Oh, Auntie!" said Charlie, **gasping** for breath. "A terrible giant little girl caught me, and hugged me and teased me, and I fell through a hole in her pocket, and—and here I am!"

"Such a lively imagination," said Charlie's auntie to his mother.

"Oh, Mother," cried Charlie, "I don't think Jane and Topsy will ever love me. I squeezed them and carried them about and bothered them so!"

Then his auntie said, "Cheer up, Charlie. Go to my sewing basket. I'll show you how to make friends with Jane and Topsy."

....

scurried moved quickly
gasping taking quick, loud breaths

She gave Charlie a ball of yarn and fixed it so that it would not unwind. Then she told Charlie to roll it round and round in front of the bookcase. Soon a little gray paw came out, and then another, and another, and soon Topsy was dancing around the room, chasing the ball of yarn.

Sometimes Topsy danced on all four legs, sometimes on his two back ones. Sometimes he jumped sideways, and sometimes he jumped straight up in the air. He seemed to be having such a good time that Jane came out from her hiding place to join the fun.

Never again did Charlie grab hold of Topsy or Jane against their will. Never again did he carry Topsy around and pay no attention when the kitten cried out, "Meow, meow!"

Since that day, Charlie has played nicely with Topsy and has done the things the kitten likes best. And now Topsy loves Charlie more than anyone else and follows him everywhere.

Moufflu

adapted from Louise de la Ramée

Lolo and Moufflu were the best of friends. Moufflu was the biggest and whitest **poodle** in the city of Florence, and Lolo was a little **lame** boy, his master. They lived with Lolo's mother and brothers and sisters under the shadow of a great **cathedral**.

They were all happy and merry, except when they did not have enough to eat, which was very often, for they were poor. Lolo's mother worked, and his brothers and sisters worked, and Lolo worked as much as he could. But as he was lame, most of the time he liked to sit by the door of the cathedral where people came and went.

One morning, as he sat on the steps in the sunshine, a strange gentleman stopped in front of him.

"What a pretty dog you have, my boy!" he said kindly.

"Moufflu is beautiful," said Lolo with pride. "You should see him on Sundays just after he is washed."

---

poodle an intelligent breed of dog
lame having a body part that is disabled so that it is difficult to move without pain
cathedral a kind of church

"How old is your dog?"

"Three years old."

"Does he do any tricks?"

"Does he!" cried Lolo. "Why, Moufflu can do anything! Would you like to see him do his tricks?"

"Very much," said the gentleman.

So Moufflu walked on two legs, danced and played dead, begged, made a wheelbarrow of himself, and did everything else you could imagine.

The strange gentleman clapped his hands. "Your dog is very clever," he said. "Would you be willing to bring him to please a sick child I have at home?"

Lolo smiled and said he would. The man told him to come to a great hotel, and he dropped two **francs** into Lolo's hand. "Come this afternoon," he said.

....

francs money used in France

Lolo hurried home with the coins **clasped** tightly in his hand.

"All because Moufflu did his tricks!" he cried as he gave the money to his mother. "Now you can get the shoes you need, and the coffee you miss so much every morning, and—oh, almost everything!" Two francs seemed a great deal of money to Lolo.

That afternoon, Lolo and Moufflu **trotted** to the great hotel. They were shown into a beautiful room with gilded walls and velvet furniture.

There was the strange gentleman, and there on a couch lay a pale little boy. He spoke a strange language that Lolo could not understand, but from the way he clapped his hands, Lolo knew that he liked Moufflu's tricks.

clasped held tightly
trotted walked quickly

The boy gave them crackers and cakes, which Lolo and Moufflu ate with great delight. And when at last the man sent them away, he put five francs into Lolo's hand.

As they trotted home, Lolo thought how fine it would be if a strange gentleman with a sick little boy came every day to their cathedral.

Alas for Lolo! He had not understood the sick child's cries as he and Moufflu left the room. "I want the dog! I will have the dog! I want him!" the child had cried.

The next day, the strange gentleman came to Lolo's home. He said that the sick child wanted the dog and was heartbroken when Moufflu was taken away. The man said that he would pay a thousand francs. Would they sell the dog?

The poor mother looked at the thousand francs the man held out, and then at Moufflu. Surely a dog was not worth that! Lolo loved him, to be sure, but a dog was a dog, and the children were hungry, and there was nothing in the cupboard. At last she took the money, and the man carried Moufflu away.

---

alas too bad

That night, when Lolo came home, no Moufflu ran to meet him.

"Moufflu! Moufflu!" he cried in a frightened voice. "Where is Moufflu?"

When they told him, he burst into tears.

The next day, he was very ill, and the next, and the next. All the time, he kept calling for Moufflu.

The old doctor shook his head. "What is this Moufflu the boy calls for?" he asked. "Bring him that. It is the only thing that can help him."

The poor mother was heartbroken. She had never known that Lolo loved the dog so much.

She would gladly have brought Moufflu back, but she could not. When she asked for the strange gentleman at the hotel, she was told that he had gone away. The servants shook their heads. They did not know where he had gone.

When everyone was beginning to think that Lolo would never get better, Moufflu came back. Thin and dirty and caked with mud, he came dashing up the stairs one night at sunset. He was just as happy to see them as they were to see him. It seemed as if he would knock himself over wagging his tail.

From that hour, Lolo began to get better. He would hardly let the dog out of his sight. Ten days went by, and still his mother did not dare tell him that Moufflu did not belong to them now.

No one knew where the dog had come from. Lolo's brother, Tasso, went to the hotel to look for the strange gentleman, but the man was not there.

Each day, they expected someone to come for Moufflu. The mother wanted to buy him back with the thousand francs, which she had carefully saved. But what if the strange gentleman would not sell him? She did not dare to think of it.

At last, one day when Tasso went to the hotel, he was told that the gentleman had returned. He was taken to the same room where Lolo had gone, and there he found the gentleman and the little boy.

He told them the whole story—how sick Lolo had been, how he had missed Moufflu, and how the dog had come back. He gave the thousand francs to the man and begged him to sell the dog. They would be glad to train another little dog for the boy, he said.

The man was silent a moment. Then he said, "He came alone all the way from Rome. He is a wonderful dog."

He turned to the child. "Did you understand?" he asked.

"Yes! Yes!" cried the child. "Let the little boy have Moufflu, Father. Please!"

The gentleman smiled and gave the money back to Tasso. "This is to pay for the new dog," he said. Tasso was so surprised and happy that he could hardly thank the kind man.

So Moufflu and Lolo grew strong and well and happy again. In the shadow of the cathedral, they trained another dog. The other little boy said he was just as good a dog as Moufflu, but Lolo knew better.

Black Beauty

adapted from the novel by Anna Sewell

The first place that I can remember well was a large, pleasant meadow. There were six young colts in the meadow besides my mother and me. They were much older than I was. Some of them were nearly as large as grown-up horses.

My master would not sell me till I was four years old. He said colts ought not to work like horses until they were quite grown up.

When I was four years old, Squire Gordon came to look at me. He **examined** my eyes, my mouth, and my legs. Then I had to walk, **trot**, and **gallop** for him.

He seemed to like me and said, "When he has been broken in, he will do very well."

As everyone may not know what breaking in is, I shall describe it. I had, of course, been used to being led about in the fields by a halter. Now, however, I must have a bit and a bridle.

My master gave me some oats, as usual, and after much **coaxing** he put the bit in my mouth and the bridle on my head. It was most **unpleasant**.

A great piece of cold, hard steel was pushed into my mouth, between my teeth, and over my tongue. Then straps were fastened over my nose and chin, so that I could not get rid of the hard thing.

examined studied or looked at closely
trot run slowly
gallop run fast (by a horse)
coaxing asking for something in a gentle way
unpleasant not enjoyable

Next came the saddle, but that was not half so bad. My master put it on my back very gently, while old Daniel held my head. Then I had a few oats, and he led me about the field.

This he did every day, until I began to look for the oats and the saddle.

At length, one morning, my master got on my back and rode me around the meadow. It certainly did feel queer, but I was proud to carry my master and soon grew used to the feeling.

After that, I was taken to the blacksmith's to be **shod**. My master went with me and talked to me so that I should not be frightened. The blacksmith took my feet, one after the other, and cut away some of the hoof.

....
shod fit with shoes

The cutting did not hurt at all. I stood on three legs and let the smith hold one foot in his hand. Then he took the heavy iron shoes and nailed them to my feet.

That did not hurt either, but the shoes made my feet feel very stiff and heavy. Later I found that these shoes kept my feet from being hurt by the stony roads.

When my master was ready to teach me to draw the carriage, there were more new things to wear. I shall not name all of them.

The worst of these was the stiff little strap called the **crupper**. That went under my tail. I hated it. To have my long tail doubled up and poked through that strap was as bad as the bit.

crupper a loop, usually made of padded leather, that circles the horse's tail and is attached by one or two straps to the back of a horse's saddle or driving harness to keep the saddle or harness in place

I must not forget one important part of my training. My master sent me for two weeks to a meadow near a railroad track. Here were some sheep and cows, and I was turned in among them.

I shall never forget the first train that ran by. I was feeding quietly when I heard a strange sound. Before I knew it, a long, black train flew by. I turned and galloped to the other side of the meadow and stood there snorting with fear. The cows, however, went on eating and hardly raised their heads.

For the first few days, I could not eat in peace because of these trains. Later I found they never came into the fields or hurt me in any way. Then I was less frightened, and soon I paid no more attention than the cows did.

As the days passed, I grew more and more used to my work. My coat was brushed every day until it shone like satin, and my mane and tail were smooth and clean.

In time I became used to everything and could do my work as well as my mother. In fact, my master often drove me in a double harness with my mother. She was steady and could teach me much.

She told me the better I behaved, the better I should be treated, and that it was wisest always to do my best to please my master. "But," said she, "there are a great many kinds of men. There are good, thoughtful men like our master, who any horse may be proud to serve. And there are bad, cruel men, who never ought to have a horse or dog to call their own. And there are a great many foolish men, who never trouble themselves to think; these spoil more horses than all. I hope you will fall into good hands, but a horse never knows who may buy him. It is all a chance for us. But still I say, do your best wherever it is, and keep up your good name."

At last, early in May, Squire Gordon sent a man to bring me to his home at Birtwick Park. My master came to the stable to say good-bye. I put my nose in his hand, and he patted my neck.

"Good-bye," he said. "Be a good horse and always do your best."

Then I was led out of the stable and away from my first home.

One night, I had eaten my hay and I was lying on my straw asleep. Suddenly I was roused by the loud ringing of the stable bell. I heard the **coachman**, John Manly, open the door of his cottage near my stable. Then I heard the sound of his feet running down to the house.

He was back again in no time. He unlocked the stable door and called out, "Wake up, Beauty! You must go now, if ever you did."

Almost before I could think, he had the saddle on my back and the bridle on my head. He ran for his coat and took me at a quick trot to the front door of the house. Squire Gordon stood there with a lamp in his hand.

coachman a man who drives a coach or carriage

"Now, John," he said, "ride for your life—that is, for the life of your **mistress**. Give this note to Dr. White, and be back as soon as you can."

John said, "Yes, sir," and was on my back in an **instant**.

The gardener, who lived near the gate, had heard the bell ring. He had the gate open, and away we went, through the park and the village, till we came to the **tollgate**.

John called very loudly and thumped on the door. The man was soon out and flung open the gate.

"Now," said John, "keep the gate open for the doctor. Here is the money."

mistress a woman who is in charge of a house

instant moment

tollgate a stopping point in a road where a guard collects payment for entry

There lay before us a long piece of level road. John said to me, "Now, Beauty, do your best," and so I did. I wanted neither whip nor spur. For two miles, I galloped as fast as I could lay my feet to the ground.

When we came to the bridge, John pulled me up a little and patted my neck. He would have let me go slower, but I was off again, as fast as before. On and on we went, until, at the end of eight miles, we came to the town.

It was all quite still, except for the clatter of my feet on the stones. Everybody was asleep. The church clock struck three as we drew up at Dr. White's door.

John rang the bell twice and then knocked at the door like thunder. A window opened, and Dr. White put his head out.

"What do you want?" he called.

"Mrs. Gordon is very sick. Master thinks she will die if you do not get there. Here is a note."

The doctor shut the window and was soon at the door.

"The worst of it is that my horse has been out all day and is very tired," he said. "Can I have your horse?"

"He has come at a gallop nearly all the way, sir, but I think my master would be willing," said John.

"All right," said the doctor, "I will soon be ready."

The doctor came out with his riding whip.

"You need not take that, sir," said John. "Black Beauty will go till he drops. Take care of him, sir, if you can. I should not like any harm to come to him."

"No, no, John," said the doctor, "I hope not." And in a minute, we had left John far behind.

I shall not tell you about our way back. The doctor was a heavier man than John, and not so good a rider. However, I did my best. The man at the tollgate had it open, and soon we were in the park.

My master was at the door, for he had heard us coming. The doctor went into the house with him, and Joe, the new stable boy, led me to the stable.

I was glad to get home. My legs shook under me, and I could only stand and pant. Joe was young and as yet he knew little about horses. I am sure he did the best he knew.

He rubbed my legs and chest, but he did not put my warm cloth on me. He thought I was hot so I should not like it.

Then he gave me cold water and some hay and corn. Thinking he had done right, he went away.

Soon I began to shake and **tremble** with cold. Oh, how I wished for my warm cloth! I wished for John, too, but he had eight miles to walk.

After a long while I heard him at the door, and I gave a low **moan**.

He was at my side in a moment. I could not tell him how I felt, but he seemed to understand. He covered me with two or three warm cloths and then ran to the house for hot water. He made me some warm **gruel**, which I drank, and after that I think I must have gone to sleep.

....

tremble shake with fear
moan a long, low sound of sadness
gruel a watery porridge

I do not know how long I was ill. John nursed me night and day. He would get up two or three times in the night to come to me. My master, too, often came to see me. "My poor Beauty," he said one day, "my good horse, you saved your mistress's life, Beauty; yes, you saved her life."

I was very glad to hear that. It seems the doctor had said if we had been a little longer, my mistress would have died.

John told my master he never saw a horse go so fast in his life. He said it seemed as if the horse knew what was the matter. Of course I did. At least I knew that John and I must go at the top of our speed, and that it was for the sake of the mistress. ❧

BLACK BEAUTY

And I knew
The lights
Were MY CAT'S EYES
In the dark.

The Elephant

by Annette Wynne

The elephant is very large
And clumsy as a wooden barge,
With legs like tree trunks, yet he's mild
And gentle as a little child.

The elephant walks far away
And sees strange children in their play,
And carries logs and iron bars
As easily as motor cars.

The elephant's a great big beast—
Not beautiful, but good, at least,
Strong as a tree, but withal mild
And gentle as a little child.

barge a large boat, usually with a flat bottom, used to carry
goods on rivers and other waterways

mild gentle; calm

withal an old-fashioned word meaning "besides" or "on the other hand"

THE ELEPHANT

The **Silent Snake**

by Anonymous

The birds go fluttering in the air,
The rabbits run and skip,
Brown squirrels race along the **bough**,
The **mayflies** rise and dip;
But while these creatures play and leap,
The silent snake goes creepy-**creep**!

The birds, they sing and whistle loud,
The busy insects hum,
The squirrels chat, the frogs say "Croak!"
But the snake is always **dumb**.
With not a sound through grasses deep,
The silent snake goes creepy-creep!

bough a branch of a tree
mayflies flying insects
creep to move with the body close to the ground;
to move slowly or quietly
dumb not able to speak; mute

The **Necklace** *of* **Truth**

adapted from the story by Jean Mace

There once was a little girl named Pearl, who had the bad habit of telling lies. For a long time, her father and mother did not find this out, but at last they saw that she very often said things that were not true.

Now at this time—for it was long, long ago—there was a wonderful man named Merlin. He could do such strange things, and was so wise, that he was called a wizard.

Merlin was one of the greatest friends of truth that ever lived. For this reason, children who told lies were often brought to him so that he might **cure** them of this bad habit.

"Let us take our child to the wonderful wizard," said Pearl's father.

And the mother said, "Yes, let us take her to Merlin. He will cure her!"

So Pearl's parents went to the palace where Merlin lived.

....

cure to free from something harmful

When they reached Merlin's palace, the mother began to tell the wise old man what was the matter with her child. "I know very well what is the matter with her, my dear madam," said Merlin. "Your child is one of the greatest liars in the world."

How did he know this? I cannot say, but this wizard could tell a liar, even though many miles away.

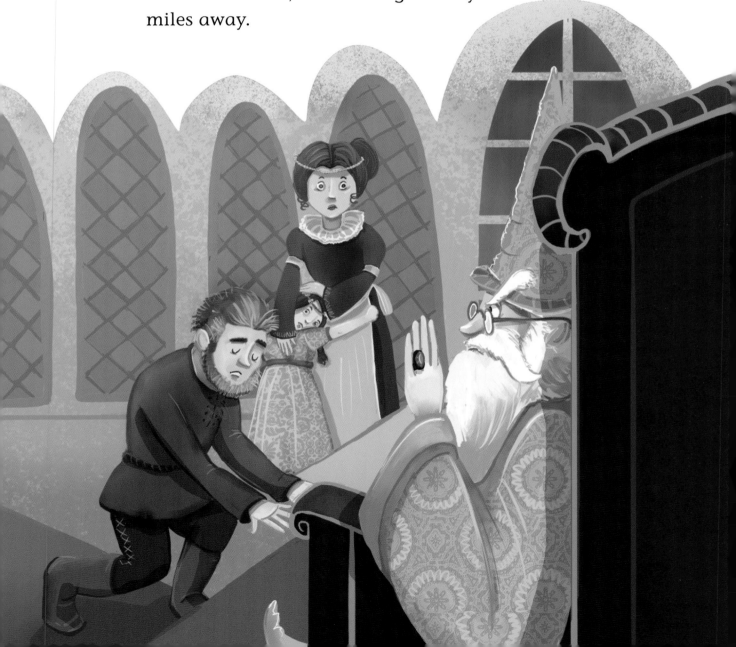

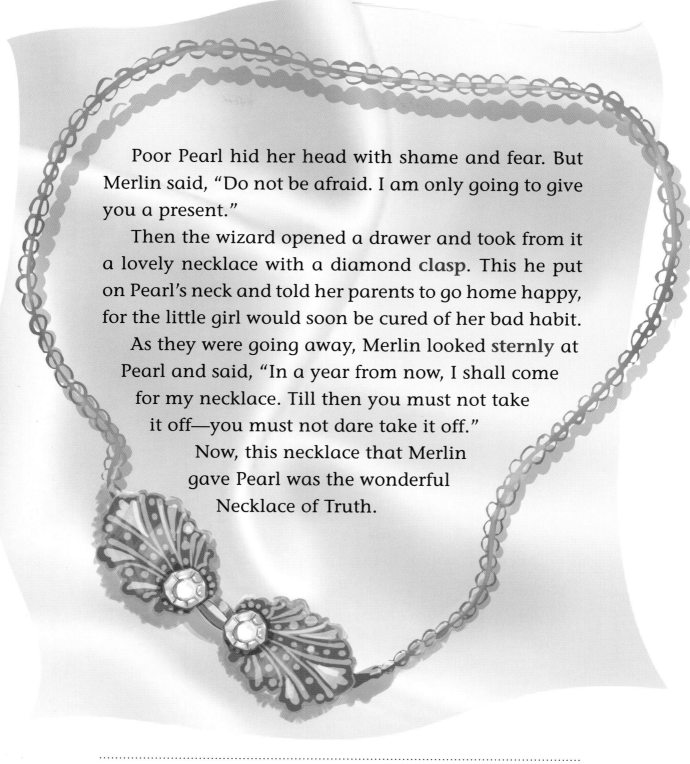

Poor Pearl hid her head with shame and fear. But Merlin said, "Do not be afraid. I am only going to give you a present."

Then the wizard opened a drawer and took from it a lovely necklace with a diamond **clasp**. This he put on Pearl's neck and told her parents to go home happy, for the little girl would soon be cured of her bad habit.

As they were going away, Merlin looked **sternly** at Pearl and said, "In a year from now, I shall come for my necklace. Till then you must not take it off—you must not dare take it off."

Now, this necklace that Merlin gave Pearl was the wonderful Necklace of Truth.

clasp a kind of hook that holds two things together
sternly in a firm way

The next day, Pearl went out to play. When her neighbors saw her beautiful necklace, they crowded around her.

"Oh, what a lovely necklace! Where did you get it, Pearl?"

"My father gave it to me for a Christmas present," said Pearl. (This, you know, was a **falsehood**.)

"Oh, look, look!" cried the children. "The diamond has turned dim!"

---

falsehood a lie

Pearl looked down at her lovely necklace and saw that the diamond clasp had changed to glass. Then she was very much afraid, and said, "I will tell you the truth. The wizard Merlin gave it to me."

At once the diamond was as bright as before.

The girls now began to laugh, because they knew that only children who told lies were sent to Merlin.

"You need not laugh," said Pearl. "Merlin sent a lovely coach to bring us. It was drawn by six white horses, and was lined with satin and had gold tassels; and his palace is all built of gems; and he **praised** me because I tell the truth." (But these were all fibs, as you know.)

She stopped, for the children were laughing all the time she was speaking. Then she looked at her necklace—and what do you think? It hung down to the ground! With each lie she had told, the necklace had stretched more and more.

praised spoke highly of

"You are stretching the truth!" cried the little girls.

Then Pearl **confessed** that all she had told them was false. At once the necklace changed to its right size.

"But what did Merlin say when he gave you the necklace?" the girls asked.

"He said it was a present for a truthful"—but Pearl could not go on speaking. The necklace became so short that it nearly choked her.

"Oh no!" sobbed Pearl. "He said I was—I was—the greatest liar in the world."

The girls did not laugh now. They were sorry for poor Pearl when they saw her **weeping**.

So at last Pearl was cured. She saw how wrong and how foolish it is to tell falsehoods. "Never more will I tell a lie," said she. And she kept her word.

Before the year was ended, Merlin came for his necklace. He knew that Pearl did not need it now, and he wanted it for a little boy.

---

confessed admitted wrongdoing
weeping crying very hard

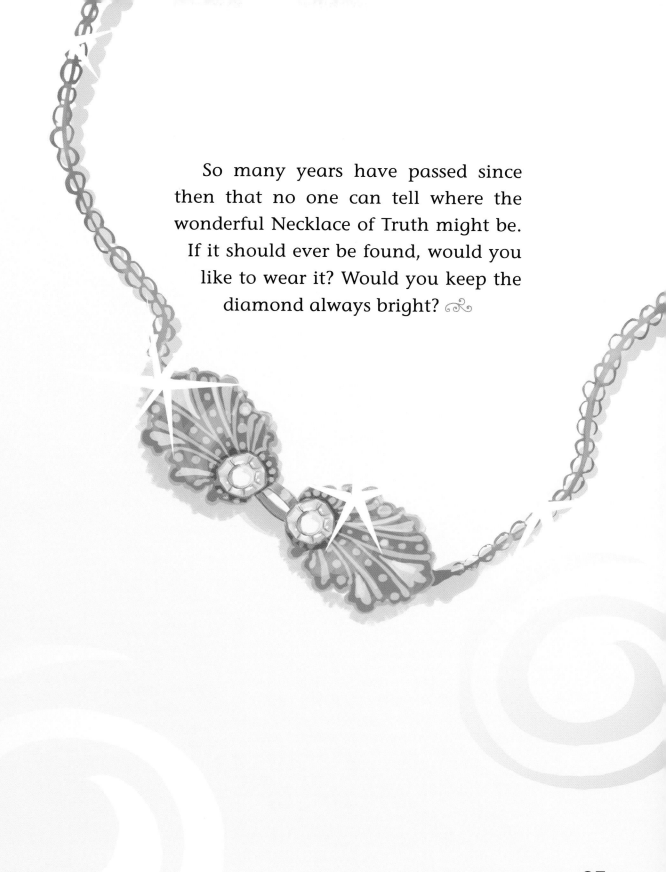

So many years have passed since then that no one can tell where the wonderful Necklace of Truth might be. If it should ever be found, would you like to wear it? Would you keep the diamond always bright?

The Stone in the Road

Early one morning, a sturdy old farmer came along the highway with his oxcart loaded with corn. "Oh, these lazy people!" he cried, driving his oxen to one side of the road. "Here is this big stone right in the middle of the road, and nobody will take the trouble to move it!" So he went on his way, **scolding** about the laziness of other people.

Then along came a soldier with a bright feather in his hat and a big sword at his side. He held his head

---

scolding finding fault with; saying unpleasant things

high in the air and sang a merry song. Of course he did not see the stone in the road, but **stumbled** over it and fell flat in the dust.

When he had picked himself up, he began to scold about the country people.

"The stupid things!" he said. "Don't they know any better than to leave a stone in the road?"

An hour later, six **merchants** came down the road with their goods on pack horses, on their way to the fair. When they came to the stone, they carefully drove their horses around it.

stumbled tripped
merchants people who buy and sell things

"Did anyone ever see such a thing?" they said. "There is that big stone in the road, and not one man in all the country will pick it up!"

The stone lay there for three weeks. It was in everybody's way. Wouldn't you think that someone might have taken the trouble to move it? But no! Each man **grumbled** about it and left it for somebody else to move.

Then one day the king sent word to all his people to meet on the highway, for he had something to tell them.

Soon a great crowd of men and women gathered in the road. The farmer was there, and so were the merchants and the soldier.

"I hope the king will now find out what lazy people he has around him," said the soldier.

"I shall not be surprised," said the farmer, "if the king has something to say about how these people leave stones in the road."

At length the sound of a horn was heard, and the king came riding toward the crowd. When he reached the stone, he said, "My friends, I put this stone in the road three weeks ago. Each and every one of you has seen it. Each man has scolded his neighbor, but not one of you has taken the trouble to move the stone.

grumbled complained

Then the king got down from his horse and rolled the stone over. Underneath it, in a round, hollow place, lay a small iron box. He held up the box so that the people might see the piece of paper **fastened** to it. On the paper were written these words:

For the one who lifts the stone.

The king opened the box and turned it upside down. Out fell a beautiful gold ring and twenty bright coins.

"These," said he, "were waiting for the man who would move the stone instead of finding fault with his neighbors."

....
fastened attached

Bruce *and the* Spider

Long ago, Robert Bruce, the king of Scotland, was hiding one day in a little hut that lay deep in the forest. He was all alone and very **discouraged**. He had been fighting many battles with the enemies of Scotland and had lost every battle. His soldiers had been killed or driven to take **refuge** in the mountains, as the king himself was now doing. He was hungry and homeless. He had no food and no place of shelter but a **mean** hut.

"There is no use in trying to free Scotland now," thought the king. "Our enemies are too strong. I might as well give up the struggle."

Just then he saw a spider trying to spin a web between two **rafters**. She would fasten one end of her thread to a rafter and then swing herself across to the other rafter. She seemed to find this very hard, for each time the thread broke, she would have to begin all over again.

---

discouraged feeling hopeless; thinking you cannot succeed
refuge shelter; protection
mean run down or poorly made
rafters beams, usually made of wood, that hold up a roof

Bruce sat watching her, and he wondered how long she would keep trying before she gave up. Six times the spider tried to fasten her thread, and six times she failed.

"You are a brave and patient spider," thought the king. "You do not give up as soon as I do. I will watch you try the seventh time. If you succeed, I too will risk my seventh battle."

Once more the spider swung her tiny thread to the opposite rafter, and this time it held fast.

"You have taught me a lesson, little spider," said Bruce. "I will gather my army and try once more to drive away the enemies of Scotland."

So the king stood again at the head of his army, and he fought as he had never fought before. This time, he won the battle and made his country free. ❧

The **Calabash Kids**
A Tale of Tanzania

retold by Aaron Shepard

Characters

NARRATORS 1–4

SHINDO

CHIEFTAIN

CHILDREN 1–7

KITETE

WOMEN 1–3

Place

A VILLAGE IN TANZANIA

NARRATOR 1: Once, there was a woman named Shindo, who lived in a village at the foot of a snow-capped mountain.

NARRATOR 4: Her husband had died, and she had no children, so she was very lonely.

NARRATOR 2: And, she was always tired, too, for she had no one to help with the chores.

NARRATOR 3: All on her own, she

NARRATOR 1: cleaned the hut,

NARRATOR 4: cleaned the yard,

NARRATOR 2: tended the chickens,

NARRATOR 3: washed her clothes in the river,

NARRATOR 1: carried water,

NARRATOR 4: cut firewood,

NARRATOR 2: and cooked her **solitary** meals.

NARRATOR 3: At the end of each day, Shindo **gazed** up at the snowy **peak** and prayed.

SHINDO: Great Mountain Spirit! My work is too hard. Send me help!

NARRATOR 1: One day, Shindo was weeding her small field by the river, where she grew vegetables and bananas and **gourds**. Suddenly, a noble chieftain appeared beside her.

CHIEFTAIN: I am a **messenger** from the Great Mountain Spirit.

NARRATOR 1: He handed the **astonished** woman some gourd seeds.

CHIEFTAIN: Plant these carefully. They are the answer to your prayers.

···

solitary lonely
gazed looked
peak mountaintop
gourds fruits with hard outsides, such as pumpkins
messenger person who brings messages or information
astonished very surprised

NARRATOR 2: Then, the chieftain **vanished.**

SHINDO: (*skeptically, looking at the seeds in her hand*)
What help could I get from a handful of seeds?

....

vanished disappeared
skeptically doubtfully

NARRATOR 3: Still, she planted and tended them as carefully as she could.

NARRATOR 1: Shindo was **amazed** at how quickly the seeds grew. In just a week, long vines trailed over the ground, and ripe gourds hung from them.

NARRATOR 4: Shindo brought the gourds home, sliced off the tops, and scooped out the **pulp**. Then, she laid the gourds on the rafters of her hut to dry.

NARRATOR 2: When they hardened, she could sell them at the market as **calabashes**, to be made into bowls and jugs.

NARRATOR 3: One fine gourd Shindo set by the cook fire. This one she wanted to use herself, and she hoped it would dry faster.

NARRATOR 1: The next morning, Shindo went off again to tend her field.

NARRATOR 4: But, meanwhile, back in the hut,

NARRATOR 2: the gourds began to change.

NARRATOR 3: They sprouted heads,

NARRATOR 1: then arms,

NARRATOR 4: then legs.

....

amazed filled with wonder
pulp soft, fleshy part of a fruit or vegetable
calabashes hard-shelled fruits, shaped like a bottle

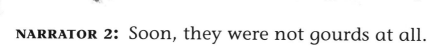

NARRATOR 2: Soon, they were not gourds at all.

NARRATOR 3: They were—

ALL NARRATORS: children!

NARRATOR 1: One boy lay by the fire, where Shindo had put the fine gourd.

NARRATOR 4: The other children called to him from the **rafters**.

....

rafters beams, usually made of wood, that hold up a roof

CHILDREN: *Ki-te-te, come help us!*
We'll work for our mother.
Come help us, Ki-te-te,
Our favorite brother!

NARRATOR 2: Kitete helped his brothers and sisters down from the rafters.

NARRATOR 3: Then, the children started quickly on the chores.

CHILD 1: Clean the hut!

CHILD 2: Clean the yard!

CHILD 3: Feed the chickens!

CHILD 4: Wash the clothes!

CHILD 5: Carry the water!

CHILD 6: Cut the wood!

CHILD 7: Cook the meal!

NARRATOR 1: All joined in but Kitete.

NARRATOR 4: Drying by the fire had made the boy slow-witted. So, he just sat there, smiling widely.

NARRATOR 2: When the work was done, Kitete helped the others climb back on the rafters.

NARRATOR 3: Then, they all turned again into gourds.

NARRATOR 1: That afternoon, as Shindo returned home, the other women of the village called to her.

WOMAN 1: Who were those children in your yard today?

WOMAN 2: Where did they come from?

WOMAN 3: Why were they doing your chores?

SHINDO: (*angrily*) What children? Are you all making fun of me?

NARRATOR 4: But, when she reached her hut, she was **astounded**.

NARRATOR 2: The work was done, and even her meal was ready!

NARRATOR 3: She could not imagine who had helped her.

NARRATOR 1: The same thing happened the next day. As soon as Shindo had gone off, the gourds turned into children,

NARRATOR 4: with heads

NARRATOR 2: and arms

NARRATOR 3: and legs.

....

astounded amazed

NARRATOR 3: That is, all were helpful but Kitete, who stayed by the fire with his simple-minded smile.

NARRATOR 1: Most of the time, Shindo didn't mind.

NARRATOR 4: In fact, Kitete was really her favorite, because he was like a sweet baby.

NARRATOR 2: But sometimes, when she was tired or unhappy about something else, she would get annoyed and yell at him.

SHINDO: You useless child! Why can't you be smart like your brothers and sisters, and work as hard as they do?

NARRATOR 3: Kitete would only grin back at her.

NARRATOR 1: One day, Shindo was out in the yard, cutting vegetables for a stew. As she carried the pot from the bright sunlight into the hut, she tripped over Kitete.

NARRATOR 4: She fell, and the clay pot shattered. Vegetables and water streamed everywhere.

SHINDO: (*getting up, screaming at him*) Stupid boy! Haven't I told you to stay out of my way? (*derisively*) But, what can I expect? You're not a real child at all. You're nothing but a calabash!

NARRATOR 2: The very next moment, Kitete was no longer there.

NARRATOR 3: In his place was a gourd.

SHINDO: (*shrieking*) What have I done? I didn't mean what I said! You're not a calabash, you're my own **darling** son!

NARRATOR 1: The other children came crowding into the hut.

SHINDO: Oh, children, please do something!

NARRATOR 4: They looked at each other for a moment.

NARRATOR 2: Then, over each other they climbed, **scampering** up on the rafters.

NARRATOR 3: When the last child had been helped up by Shindo, they called out one last time,

CHILDREN: *Ki-te-te, come help us!*
We'll work for our mother.
Come help us, Ki-te-te,
OUR FAVORITE BROTHER!

NARRATOR 1: For a long moment, nothing happened.

NARRATOR 4: Then, slowly,

NARRATOR 2: the gourd began to change.

NARRATOR 3: It sprouted a head,

NARRATOR 1: then arms,

NARRATOR 4: then legs.

---

shrieking making a high-pitched, loud sound
darling dear
scampering hurrying

NARRATOR 2: At last, it was not a gourd at all.

NARRATOR 3: It was—

SHINDO & CHILDREN: (*shouting happily, as SHINDO hugs him*) Kitete!

NARRATOR 1: Shindo learned her lesson.

NARRATOR 4: Ever after, she was very careful what she called her children.

NARRATOR 2: And so, they gave her comfort and happiness,

NARRATOR 3: all the rest of her days.

April Rain Song

by Langston Hughes

Let the rain kiss you.
Let the rain beat upon your head
   with silver liquid drops.
Let the rain sing you a **lullaby**.

lullaby a song meant to help a child fall asleep

The rain makes still pools on the sidewalk.
The rain makes running pools in the **gutter**.
The rain plays a little sleep-song on our roof
  at night—

And I love the rain.

---

gutter a low area along the edge of a street where water can run off

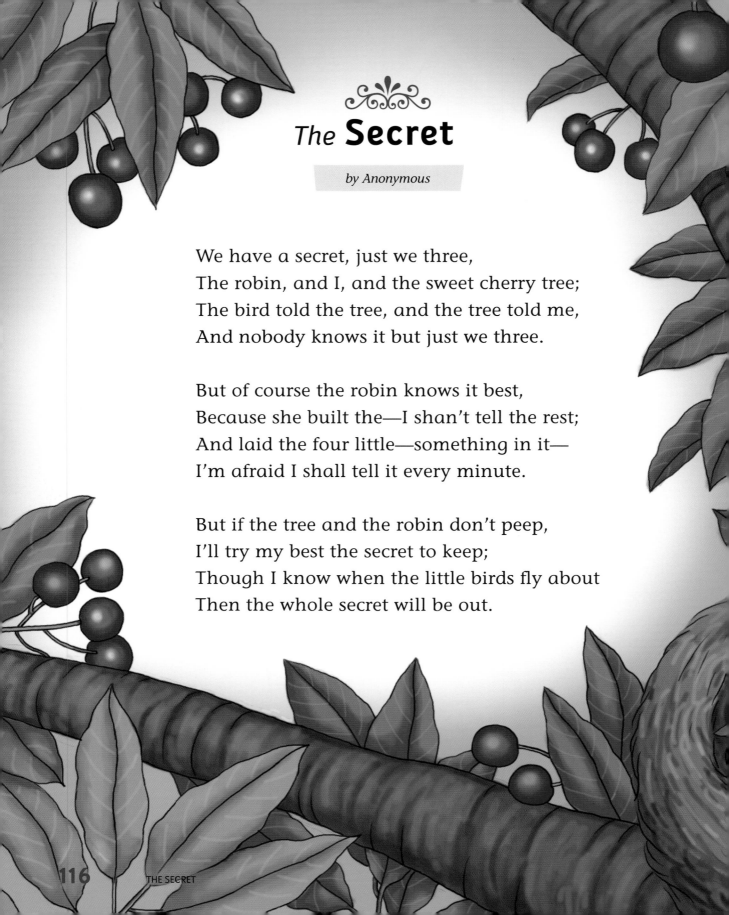

The Secret

by Anonymous

We have a secret, just we three,
The robin, and I, and the sweet cherry tree;
The bird told the tree, and the tree told me,
And nobody knows it but just we three.

But of course the robin knows it best,
Because she built the—I shan't tell the rest;
And laid the four little—something in it—
I'm afraid I shall tell it every minute.

But if the tree and the robin don't peep,
I'll try my best the secret to keep;
Though I know when the little birds fly about
Then the whole secret will be out.

The Building of the Nest

by Margaret E. Sangster

They'll come again to the apple tree—
Robin and all the rest—
When the **orchard** branches are fair to see,
In the snow of the **blossom** dressed;
And the prettiest thing in the world will be
The building of the nest.
Weaving it well, so round and trim,
Hollowing it with care,
Nothing too far away for him,
Nothing for her too **fair**,
Hanging it safe on the topmost **limb**,
Their castle in the air.

....

orchard land used for growing fruit or nut trees, or the large group of trees that grow the fruits

blossom a flower

weaving lacing together strands or pieces

fair pleasant to look at; lovely

limb tree branch

Ah! mother bird, you'll have **weary** days
When the eggs are under your breast,
And shadow may darken the dancing rays
When the wee ones leave the nest;
But they'll find their wings in a glad **amaze**,
And God will see to the rest.

weary very tired
amaze an old-fashioned word for "a surprise"

So come to the trees with all your **train**
When the apple blossoms blow;
Through the April shimmer of sun and rain,
Go flying to and **fro**;
And sing to our hearts as we watch again
Your fairy building grow.

....

train a line of followers
fro from

The *Raindrop's* Ride

by Anonymous

Some little drops of water
Whose home was in the sea,
To go upon a journey
Once happened to agree.

A white cloud was their carriage;
Their horse, a playful breeze;
And over town and country
They rode along at ease.

But oh! there were so many,
At last the carriage broke,
And to the ground came tumbling
Those frightened little folk.

Among the grass and flowers
They then were forced to **roam**,
Until a **brooklet** found them
And carried them all home.

roam to wander; to travel from place to place without a plan
brooklet a small brook

As he walked beside the canal, he noticed how the rains had **swollen** the waters, and how they beat against the side of the dike, and he thought of his father's gates.

"I am glad they are so strong," he said to himself. "If they gave way, what would become of us? These fields would be covered with water. Father always calls them the 'angry waters.' I suppose he thinks they are angry at him for keeping them out so long."

As he walked along, he sometimes stopped to pick the pretty blue flowers that grew beside the road, or to

swollen made something grow to a larger-than-normal size

listen to the rabbits' soft tread as they rustled through the grass. He smiled as he thought of his visit to the blind man, who was always so glad to be visited.

Suddenly he noticed that the sun was setting and that it was growing dark. "Mother will be watching for me," he thought, and he began to run toward home.

Just then he heard a noise. It was a dripping, trickling sound. He stopped and looked down. There was a small hole in the dike, through which a tiny stream was flowing.

Any child in Holland is frightened at the thought of a leak in the dike. Peter understood the danger at once. If the water ran through a little hole, it would soon make a larger one, and the whole country would be flooded. In a moment he saw what he must do. Throwing away his flowers, he climbed down the side of the dike and **thrust** his finger into the tiny hole.

The flowing of the water was stopped!

"Oho!" he said to himself. "The angry waters must stay back now. I can keep them back with my finger. Holland shall not be drowned while I am here."

This was all very well at first, but it soon grew dark and cold. The little fellow shouted, "Hello! Is anyone there? Come here!" But no one heard him; no one came to help him.

It grew still colder. His arm **ached** and began to grow stiff and **numb**. He shouted again, "Will no one come? Mother! Mother!"

Many times since sunset, his mother had looked **anxiously** along the dike road for her little boy. Now she had closed and locked the cottage door, thinking that Peter was spending the night with his blind friend, and that she would scold him in the morning for staying away from home without her permission.

....

thrust forced into
ached hurt badly
numb lost feeling
anxiously worriedly; nervously

Peter tried to whistle, but his teeth chattered with cold. He thought of his brother and sister in their warm beds, and of his dear father and mother. "I must not let them be drowned," he thought. "I must stay here until someone comes, if I have to stay all night."

The moon and stars looked down on the child **crouching** on a stone on the side of the dike. His head was bent and his eyes were closed, but he was not asleep, for every now and then he rubbed the hand that was holding back the angry sea.

In the early morning, a **laborer** going to his work thought he heard a groan as he walked along on the top of the dike. Bending down, he saw the child, and called to him: "What is the matter, boy? Are you hurt? Why are you sitting there?"

"I am keeping the water from running in," was the answer of the little hero. "Tell them to come quickly."

crouching bending the lower body at the knees
laborer worker

William Tell

Many, many years ago, a cruel **tyrant** named Gessler ruled Switzerland. He was a **stern**, hard ruler. He hated the Swiss people, and most of all he hated a man named William Tell.

Tell was a strong, brave man. No one else could shoot an arrow as straight as he could. No one else could sail a boat as skillfully over a stormy lake. Gessler hated William Tell because Tell was brave and true, and because he loved freedom and right.

One day, Tell and his young son Albert fell into the power of Gessler's soldiers. The tyrant was glad to hear of this. He tried to think of the cruelest way to punish Tell.

"Let the man shoot at an apple a hundred **paces** away," he said. "If he can hit it, I will spare his life and his son's." Then with a **sneer**, he added, "And the apple must rest on his son's head."

Tell refused to try to save his son's life in such a way. He was very skillful, but he could not be sure of hitting an apple so far away without harming the boy.

tyrant a mean ruler
stern harsh, mean
paces steps made while walking
sneer a fake smile that shows dislike

Albert was a brave boy. He begged his father to try. "You will not hit me, Father," he said. "I know you will hit the apple, and then we shall both be free."

Tell again refused to try. At last Gessler cried angrily, "Come, make the **trial**. If you do not, your boy shall die at once. I give you one chance to save his life. Use it."

There was nothing else that Tell could do.

The soldiers marked off a hundred paces. They led Albert forward and placed the apple on his head. The boy stood there, straight and fearless.

Tell chose two arrows. He placed one in his belt and the other on his bow. Then he took aim carefully.

trial test

The arrow hissed through the air and flew straight to the core of the apple. The boy was **unharmed**.

"Father!" he cried, "I'm safe!" He ran to his father and clasped him about the neck.

Before Tell could move, Gessler asked, "Why did you place that second arrow in your belt?"

"To kill you, if I had **slain** my boy," answered Tell.

Gessler was very angry. "I have promised you your life," he said, "but you shall spend it in darkness, in a prison where neither sun nor moon can shine upon you."

---

unharmed not hurt
slain killed

Turning to his soldiers, he added, "Let the boy go, but take the man to my boat."

Instantly the soldiers seized William Tell and bound him. They carried him to the small boat in which Gessler was to return to his castle.

Soon after they set sail, a great storm sprang up. The winds and waves tossed the boat from side to side. Gessler's men were frightened, for not one of them could manage the boat in such a furious storm.

Gessler feared that they would all be drowned. He knew that William Tell could steer the boat safely, so at last he gave orders that the prisoner should be unbound.

Tell headed the boat straight for land. As it touched the shore, he gave a great leap to the rocks and dashed away.

The boat slipped back into deep water, so that Gessler and the others could not follow him. While they were tossing about on the lake, Tell escaped, and before the storm was over, he was out of reach of the tyrant. ❧

The Stone-Cutter

When Taro was a little boy, he said, "If I ever grow up to be a stone-cutter and can go up with the men in the morning and cut the great rocks from the mountainside, I shall be happy."

Years went by, and Taro grew big and strong. One morning, he took his hammer and set out with the men to climb the mountain and cut the rock from the mountainside.

It was a happy day for Taro. All day he swung his heavy hammer and laughed to see the great rock break and the chips fly about him. All day he worked in the hot sun, and he sang as he worked.

At nighttime, he came down the mountain, tired and happy. He was glad to eat his simple supper and go to bed. And so for many days he worked and sang.

But as time went on, he was not so happy. He grew tired of rising before the sun and climbing the mountain through the cold morning mist.

As he **toiled**, the hot sun beat down upon his back. The hammer **blistered** his hands. The sharp chips cut his face. He no longer sang at his work. Taro was tired of being a stone-cutter.

toiled worked
blistered caused raised sores

One day when he had a holiday, Taro went into town. At noon he stopped to rest before a large house that stood **in the midst of** beautiful rose gardens.

The door of the house opened and a man came out. He was dressed in fine silks, as soft as spiders' webs and colored like the rainbow. Jewels sparkled on his hands. Taro watched him pick the roses and drop them into a great basket carried by a servant at his side.

"Ah, me," said Taro to himself. "This must be a very rich man."

As he walked along the stony road that night, he looked at his blistered hands and thought of the rich

---

in the midst of surrounded by

man's jeweled fingers. When he came to his little hut at the foot of the mountain, he thought of the rich man's house in the midst of rose gardens.

He looked up at the mountain, where far above him the spirit of the mountain dwelt among the clouds and mists. He thought of how he must rise the next morning before the sun and climb up there to work all day in the burning heat.

"Oh, spirit of the mountain," cried Taro, "make me a rich man, too, so that I may wear silks as fine as spiders' webs, and live in a beautiful house, and walk in rose gardens. Then shall I be happy."

The spirit of the mountain heard and smiled. That very night, the little hut **vanished**. In its place stood a large house in the midst of rose gardens.

vanished disappeared

Taro was now a very rich man. He no longer had to rise before the sun and climb the steep mountainside. He no longer had to bend all day over his work while the hot sun beat down upon his head. He could walk all day in his rose garden if he wished. But he soon became very tired of it.

One day, as he stood looking out over his garden wall, a golden chariot came dashing by. It was drawn by six white horses with golden harnesses glittering in the sun. A coachman dressed in white and gold sat up on the seat in front and cracked a golden whip.

In the chariot sat a prince, dressed in purple and cloth of gold. Over his head there was a golden umbrella to shade him from the sun, and a servant ran beside him to fan him with a golden fan.

"So this is the prince," said Taro to himself. "He is far greater than I. He rules the land for miles about. He rides in a golden chariot with a golden umbrella over his head, and a servant fans him with a golden fan."

Then Taro cried to the spirit of the mountain, "Oh, spirit, I am tired of being a rich man and walking in my rose gardens. Make me a prince who rules the land. Let me ride in a golden chariot, with a golden umbrella over my head, and a servant to fan me with a golden fan. Then I shall surely be happy."

coachman someone who drives a carriage or coach

Again the spirit of the mountain heard and smiled, and again Taro had his wish.

In the blink of an eye, he became a prince. He lived in a fine palace. He had servants dressed in white and gold, and he rode in a golden chariot with a golden umbrella over his head. He ruled the country round about, and rich and poor obeyed him.

"There is no one so great as I am," he cried. "Now I am truly happy."

One hot summer day, Taro rode through his lands in his golden chariot. The flowers **drooped** by the wayside. The fields were dry and brown. He looked up at the hot sun that poured its rays upon the dry ground.

"The sun is greater than I am," cried Taro in **sorrow**. "Oh, spirit of the mountain, what pleasure is it to be a prince and rule the land and ride in a golden chariot with a golden umbrella over my head? The sun will not obey me. I wish I were the sun. Then I should indeed be happy."

In an instant, he was the sun. He laughed as he sent his rays down upon the backs of the poor stone-cutters on the mountain. He laughed as he saw the roses **wither** in the rich men's gardens, and the princes try **in vain** to keep cool under their golden umbrellas.

....

drooped hung down
sorrow great sadness
wither dry up
in vain without success

"Ah, ha," he cried, as the earth turned brown and withered beneath his rays. "Now I am really happy. I am the strongest thing in the whole wide world."

But his happiness did not last. One day, a heavy cloud came between him and the earth. "Be gone," cried the sun, and shone its fiercest. But the cloud still floated before him.

"Be gone!" cried Taro. "Do you not see that I am the sun, the greatest thing in the world?" But still the cloud did not move.

"Alas!" cried Taro, "this cloud is greater than I. Let me be a cloud, spirit of the mountain, that I may be happy."

Once more the spirit of the mountain granted Taro's wish. He became a cloud. He hid the earth from the great sun and laughed at its rage. He sent cool showers upon the earth. The roses bloomed again. The fields grew green.

He laughed in joy at his power. He rained and rained till the rivers overflowed and the land was flooded.

Yet far up on the mountainside, the rocks stood firm. Try as he might, Taro could not move them.

He poured **torrents** of rain upon them, but they did not stir. Because of this, Taro was not happy.

"The rocks of the mountainside are **mightier** than I," he cried at last. "Oh, spirit of the mountain, let me be a rock, or I shall never be really happy."

The spirit of the mountain sighed a little. But it said, "Have thy wish. Be a rock."

It was pleasant to be a rock. The hot sun poured down its rays and the clouds dropped their rain, but the great rock stood firm. Even the prince in his golden chariot and the rich man in his rose garden could not have moved it. Surely, now Taro was happy. But his happiness did not last.

One day a man came to the mountain. Tap, tap, tap. The rock shivered as the hammer struck it. Tap, tap, tap. The rock split from side to side, and a great piece broke off and fell to the ground.

---

torrents rushes or very large amounts of water
mightier stronger, more powerful

"Oh, spirit of the mountain," cried Taro in sorrow, "man is mightier than I. Change me once more to a man, and I shall be happy and contented."

Then the spirit of the mountain smiled. "Be thou a man," it said.

So Taro became a man again. He became once more the poor stone-cutter who lived at the foot of the mountain.

Every morning he rose before the sun and climbed the mountain through banks of mist. All day he bent over his work while the hot sun beat upon his head. In the evening, very tired, he climbed down the side and was glad to eat his simple supper and go to bed.

Yet Taro was happy. He had wished for many things and had tried them all. But in the end, he knew that the life of a stone-cutter suited him best.

Once more he laughed to see the great rock break and the chips fly. And once more he sang at his work. ✀

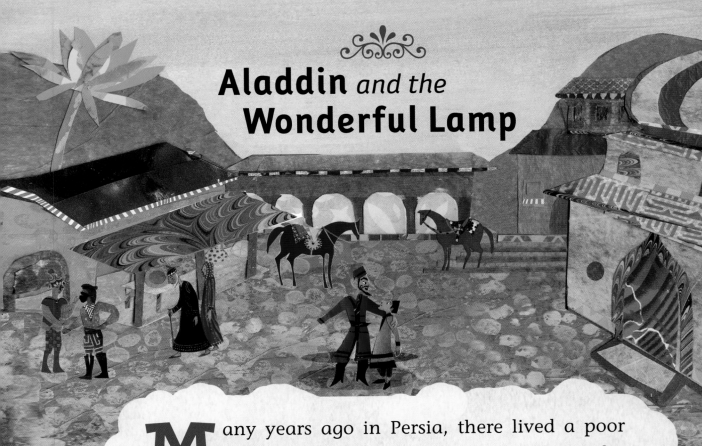

Aladdin *and the* Wonderful Lamp

Many years ago in Persia, there lived a poor **widow** and her son, Aladdin, a boy who liked to do nothing but play all day long. One day, as Aladdin was playing in the streets, a man stopped and spoke to him.

"Are you not the son of Mustapha, the tailor?" asked the stranger.

"I am, sir," replied Aladdin. "But he died long ago."

Then the stranger, who was a powerful magician, **embraced** Aladdin and cried, "My dear boy, I am your uncle. I knew you from your likeness to my brother. Run quickly and tell your mother that I am coming."

....

widow a woman whose husband has died
embraced hugged

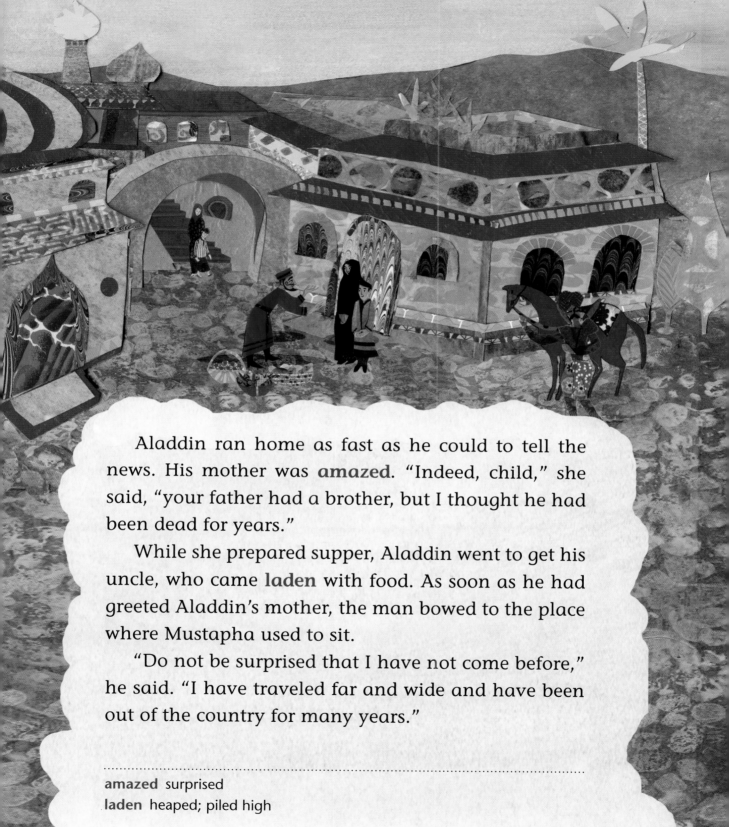

Aladdin ran home as fast as he could to tell the news. His mother was **amazed**. "Indeed, child," she said, "your father had a brother, but I thought he had been dead for years."

While she prepared supper, Aladdin went to get his uncle, who came **laden** with food. As soon as he had greeted Aladdin's mother, the man bowed to the place where Mustapha used to sit.

"Do not be surprised that I have not come before," he said. "I have traveled far and wide and have been out of the country for many years."

....

amazed surprised
laden heaped; piled high

When he heard that Aladdin had not yet learned a trade, he said that he would buy a shop for the boy and stock it with goods. "You shall become a rich merchant," he said.

The next day, he bought Aladdin a new suit of clothes and took him all over the city, where there were many wonderful things to see. At nightfall they came home, and Aladdin's mother was overjoyed to see her son looking so fine. The stranger was so good to them that she was now sure he must indeed be the brother of Mustapha.

"I do not know how to thank you enough for all your kindness," she said. "May you live many happy years."

Early the next morning, the man said to Aladdin, "Come, my boy. I will show you some fine things today."

He led Aladdin to a beautiful garden outside the city gates. After they had eaten and rested there, they traveled onward until they were a long, long way from the city.

Aladdin became so tired that he begged to go back, but the man told him pleasant stories and led him on and on. At last they came to a narrow valley between two mountains.

"We will go no farther," said the man. "I am now going to show you a sight such as no man ever saw. If you wish to see this sight, you must do as you are told. First gather some dry sticks."

Aladdin quickly brought the sticks, and the magician started a fire. Then he threw a powder on the flames and **mumbled** strange words that Aladdin could not understand.

At once, thick clouds of smoke **arose**, the earth beneath their feet trembled, and they heard a rumbling sound like thunder. Then the ground opened in front of them. There lay a large, flat stone with a brass ring in the center.

- -

mumbled said words in a low voice without speaking them clearly
arose came up from a place that already exists

Aladdin started to run away in great fright, but the magician caught him and gave him a blow that knocked him down.

"What have I done, Uncle?" cried Aladdin.

Then the man spoke kindly, saying, "Fear nothing, but obey me. Beneath this stone lies a treasure, which is to be yours. No one else may touch it. If you wish to get it, you must be brave and do just as I tell you. Grasp that brass ring with your right hand. Speak the names of your father and grandfather, and pull."

Aladdin did as he was told. The stone came up as if by magic. Beneath it were steps leading into the ground.

"Now," said the magician, "go down these steps, and you will come to three long halls. Pass through them without stopping. Be careful not to touch anything, for if you do, you will surely die. Then go straight till you come to a garden of fruit trees. You may pick some of this fruit if you wish. Then walk on till you find a lighted lamp. Pour out the oil and bring the lamp to me."

He drew a ring from his finger and gave it to Aladdin, saying, "Go down boldly, child, and do as I tell you. We shall then be rich all the rest of our lives."

Aladdin sprang quickly down the steps. He found everything just as the magician had said. He passed through the halls and the garden of beautiful trees. Without stopping and without touching anything, he went on till he found the lighted lamp. When he had poured out the oil and placed the lamp inside his coat, he began to look about him.

ALADDIN AND THE WONDERFUL LAMP

Upon the trees were fruits of every color. Some were as clear as crystal, and others were red, green, blue, or purple. All sparkled in the light, for they were really precious gems. Aladdin filled his pockets and then returned to the mouth of the cave.

The magician was kneeling at the top of the steps when Aladdin began to climb them. "Hurry!" he cried. "Give me the lamp!" He reached out to take the lamp, and at the same instant he threw some powder into the fire and **muttered** the strange words once more.

Aladdin stopped for a moment, for he could not get the lamp from the folds of his coat. "You'll have to wait until I'm out of the cave," he said. "I can't give it to you just now."

"You must!" cried the magician. "Hand the lamp to me at once!"

muttered said words in a low voice without speaking them clearly

"I will when I'm out of the cave," replied Aladdin.

But at that instant, the stone slipped back into its place. The earth closed over it, and Aladdin was left in darkness.

The magician screamed in rage. He had spoken the magic words too soon.

Now you must know that this magician was not Aladdin's uncle. He was a cruel man who had read in his books about a wonderful lamp that would make him the most powerful man in the world. He knew where to find the lamp, but the book said that it must be placed in his hands by someone else. So he had pretended to be Aladdin's uncle in order to get the boy to help him. He had planned to get the lamp and shut Aladdin in the cave. But he spoke the magic words too soon, and so put an end to his hopes.

But poor Aladdin! He was left alone in the dark cave under the ground. He was frightened nearly to death. For two long days and nights, he sat in the cave, weeping bitterly. By the third day, he was nearly **starved**. He clasped his hands in prayer, and as he did so, he rubbed the ring that the magician had given him.

In an instant, a huge and frightful genie appeared before him.

"What is thy will, master?" asked the genie. "I am the Genie of the Ring, and will obey thee in all things."

At any other time, Aladdin might have been too frightened to speak, but now he replied boldly, "Whoever you are, if you are able, take me out of this place!"

No sooner had he spoken than the earth opened, and he was once more aboveground. He set off rapidly toward home, very grateful for his escape.

When he reached home, Aladdin emptied his pockets onto the table.

"Where did you get such strange fruit, and such a curious old lamp?" asked his mother.

"I will tell you all about it," said her son, "but first I must have something to eat."

"Alas!" cried his mother. "I have neither food nor money to buy any."

---

starved dying from hunger

"Then I will sell the lamp," said Aladdin.

"At least let me polish it," said his mother. "You will get more for it."

As soon as she began to rub it, a great genie appeared and said, "I am the Genie of the Lamp. I serve the one who holds it. What is thy will?"

Aladdin's mother was so frightened that she dropped the lamp. Aladdin snatched it and spoke. "I am hungry. Bring us something to eat."

snatched grabbed

As Aladdin spoke, the genie disappeared. In a moment he returned with a silver bowl, twelve silver dishes heaped with delicious food, and two silver cups. He placed them on the table and vanished.

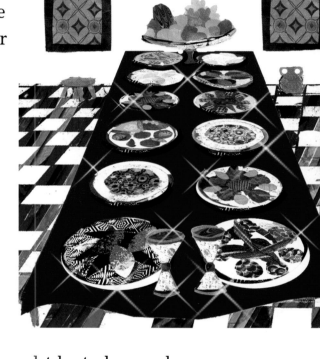

"Ah-ha!" said Aladdin. "No wonder my uncle wanted to have this lamp. It can bring me whatever I wish."

As they ate, Aladdin told his mother all that had happened in the cave. She begged him to sell the lamp and have nothing to do with the genie.

"No," said Aladdin. "Since we have learned what it can do, we will use the lamp, and also the ring, which I will always wear on my finger."

The food that the genie had brought lasted a week. When it was gone, Aladdin sold one of the silver plates. And from day to day, as they needed food, he sold the rest of the silver.

When he had nothing more to sell, Aladdin rubbed the lamp again. The genie appeared as before and brought another set of silver dishes heaped with food. Thus Aladdin and his mother were able to live in comfort for many years.

ALADDIN AND THE WONDERFUL LAMP

One day, the **sultan** ordered all the people to stay at home and close their **shutters** while his daughter, the princess, passed by on her way to the bath.

Aladdin stayed at home and closed his shutters, but he peeped through them as the princess was passing. The princess happened to raise her veil just then, and Aladdin saw her face. The moment he saw her, he loved her with all his heart.

"Mother!" he cried. "I have seen the princess, and I have made up my mind to marry her. Please go at once to the sultan and beg him to allow his daughter to marry me."

"What?" cried his mother. "You are **mad**, my boy. I cannot go to the sultan."

"Nay, you must go," said Aladdin. "Carry him this basket filled with the fruit that sparkles and shines like the most beautiful jewels. Then he will listen to you."

His mother agreed and went to the palace at once. She waited patiently, but no one even spoke to her. She went every day for a week before the sultan noticed that she was there.

"Who is the poor woman who comes here every day?" he asked. "Bring her forward."

---

sultan king
shutters window coverings
mad crazy; having lost one's senses

Aladdin's mother knelt before the throne. "Rise, good woman, and tell me what you want," said the sultan.

She told him of her son's love for the princess. "He sends you this gift of fruit," she continued, presenting the basket.

"Fruit!" exclaimed the sultan. "These are diamonds and rubies and sapphires! My daughter may marry one who sends such a gift." Then the sultan told Aladdin's mother to return in three months' time, when the wedding would take place.

When the time had passed, Aladdin again sent his mother to the sultan.

"I shall keep my word," said the sultan, "but he who marries my daughter must first send me forty baskets filled with jewels, like the one you brought before."

Aladdin's mother returned home. "You can never send the gift the sultan demands," she cried.

"Indeed I can," answered Aladdin. Then he rubbed the lamp. When the genie appeared, Aladdin told him to provide the forty baskets filled with jewels.

When the sultan received the jewels, he wished Aladdin to marry the princess without **delay**. Aladdin

---

delay waiting; putting something off

was delighted to hear the news. He ordered the genie to bring a purple robe for him to wear, as well as a white horse to ride and ten thousand gold pieces to give to the people.

At last everything was prepared. Aladdin, dressed in his purple robe, set out for the palace. As he rode along, he scattered gold coins among the people.

At the palace, the sultan greeted Aladdin joyfully and ordered the wedding feast to be prepared at once. "Not so, your majesty," said Aladdin. "I will not marry the princess until I have built her a palace."

Then he went home and once more rubbed the lamp to call forth the genie. "Build me the finest palace in the world!" ordered Aladdin. "Build it of the finest marble, set with diamonds, rubies, and other **precious** stones. In the middle, you shall build me a large hall with a dome, its four walls of gold and silver, each side having six windows. There must be stables and horses and grooms and servants. Make haste!"

precious costly; rare

The palace was finished by the next day, and the genie carried Aladdin there and showed him all his orders faithfully carried out. The genie had even laid a velvet carpet from Aladdin's palace to the sultan's.

Aladdin's mother dressed herself carefully and went to the sultan's palace. She was taken to the princess, who treated her with great honor. The princess said good-bye to her father and set out on the carpet for Aladdin's palace, with his mother at her side.

She was charmed at the sight of Aladdin, who ran to greet her.

"Princess," he said, "blame your beauty for my boldness if I have displeased you."

She told him that she willingly obeyed her father in this matter. After the wedding, Aladdin led her into the hall, where a feast was spread. They ate and danced till midnight.

For a time, Aladdin and the princess lived happily. Then trouble came to them. The magician was the cause of it. You remember that he was very angry when Aladdin did not give him the lamp. When the earth had closed over Aladdin, the magician thought, "Well, my lad, we have seen the last of you."

Months had passed, and never once did he think of Aladdin. But then, by means of his magic, he learned that the boy had escaped and had married a princess, with whom he was living in great honor and wealth.

He knew that the poor tailor's son could only have done this with the help of the Genie of the Lamp.

"I must have that lamp for myself!" cried the magician. At once he dressed himself as a merchant and traveled to the land where Aladdin lived.

When he reached the city where Aladdin lived, he walked up and down the streets. He carried a load of copper lamps. Everywhere he went, he cried, "New lamps for old! New lamps for old!"

Now it happened that Aladdin had gone hunting, and the princess sat alone near an open window. She saw the merchant and sent a servant to find out what the man was calling. The servant came back laughing. "The foolish man says he will give new lamps for old ones!" he said.

The princess scolded the servant for laughing, and then she pointed to an old lamp. "Take that old lamp," she said, "and see if the man truly wishes to trade it."

When the magician saw the lamp, he knew that it was the one for which he was searching. He took the magic lamp eagerly and gave the servant all the new ones. Then he hurried out of the city. When he was alone, he rubbed the lamp, and the genie appeared before him.

"What is thy will, master?" said the genie.

"I command you to bring me the princess and Aladdin's palace, and set us in a faraway land!" the magician cried. Instantly the palace disappeared.

The next morning, when the sultan looked out his window, there was no palace to be seen. "This must have been done by magic!" he exclaimed. He sent his soldiers to bring Aladdin home in chains. They met him riding back from the hunt and carried him to the sultan.

When Aladdin was allowed to speak, he asked, "Why have you made me a prisoner?"

"**Wretch!**" exclaimed the sultan. "Come and I will show you." Then he led Aladdin to the window and showed him that where the palace had been, there was now only an empty space.

Aladdin begged the sultan to grant him forty days in which to seek for the palace and the princess. On this condition, Aladdin was set free. He searched everywhere, but he could find no trace of the princess.

In **despair**, he **wrung** his hands. As he did so, he rubbed the magic ring. Instantly the Genie of the Ring appeared.

"I am here, master. What is thy will?" asked the genie.

wretch an unhappy person, or a person in trouble
despair hopelessness
wrung twisted together as a sign of upset

"Bring back the princess and the palace," said Aladdin.

"It is not in my power to do that," said the genie. "Only the Genie of the Lamp can bring them back."

"Then take me to the place where the palace now stands and set me down under the window of the princess."

Almost before Aladdin had finished speaking the words, he found himself beneath a window of his own palace.

"Princess! Princess!" he called.

The princess opened the window. With a cry of joy, Aladdin entered and embraced her. "Tell me," said he, "what has become of the old lamp?"

The princess shook her head sadly.

"Alas," she sighed, "a man came through the streets crying, 'New lamps for old!' I gave him the old lamp. And the next thing I knew, I was here."

"That man is a cruel magician," said Aladdin. "He has always wished to have the magic lamp. Where is he now?"

"He is still here," said the princess. "He carries the lamp in his robes during the day, and he places it under his pillow at night."

That night, while the magician was asleep, Aladdin stole softly into the room and took the lamp from under the pillow. Then he rubbed the lamp, and the genie appeared.

"I command you to carry the princess and the palace back home!" he cried.

The following morning, the sultan looked out the window. To his surprise, he saw the palace of Aladdin in the very place from which it had vanished.

After that, Aladdin and the princess lived happily for many years. When the sultan grew very old and died, they ruled in his place. And they never forgot to guard both the ring and the lamp. ❧

Mount Olympus *and* Its Inhabitants

The ancient Greeks were a wonderful people. They lived on a sunny **peninsula** in southern Europe, with the Mediterranean Sea always near them.

Their minds were filled with poetry. They imagined fantastic beings in every spot, belonging to every hill and tree and stream.

These beings were their gods. They told wonderful tales about them. They thought that the gods were everywhere and did everything. They believed that some god caused every flash of lightning, every springtime crop, every autumn harvest, and every sunset glow.

Of course, we now know the real reasons for lightning and seasons and sunsets. But we still like to hear the stories the ancient Greeks told about their gods. We call these stories *myths*. Even though we know the myths aren't true, we enjoy them because they are such wonderful stories.

---

inhabitants people or things that live in a certain place
peninsula a piece of land that sticks out and is almost surrounded by water

The ancient Greeks believed that many of their greatest gods and goddesses lived on a mountain that rose high into the clouds, called Mount Olympus. From the high peaks of Mount Olympus, the gods looked down at the world below. They helped the people they liked and hurt the people they did not like.

The Greeks believed the gods had magical powers. They could change into animals, fly through the air, or **hurl** thunderbolts from the sky.

Still, in the myths, these gods often act very much like people. They argue, they play tricks, they fall in love. Zeus was the greatest of all the gods and the king of them all. The Greeks usually pictured him as a large, strong man with long hair and a flowing beard. If he was angry, he thundered and hurled shafts of lightning to the earth.

Hera was Zeus's wife. She was a tall, beautiful goddess with yellow hair and blazing eyes. She could be charming at times, and at other times very bitter and **jealous**. She was almost the only one who was not afraid of Zeus.

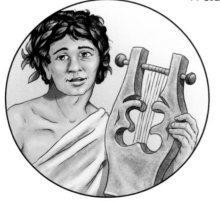

Then there was Phoebus Apollo, the god of the sun and of music. He played upon the **lyre** and sang the most beautiful songs, so that even the gods were charmed.

hurl to throw something very hard
jealous wanting what others have
lyre a musical instrument with strings

Athena was the goddess of wisdom, a very noble goddess, strong yet gentle. She gave to people the best of all gifts, wisdom.

Hephaestus, the god of fire, was the worker among the gods. He built the palaces in which the gods lived. He made the armor they wore, the chariots they drove, and the tables from which they ate at their **banquets**. If the gods wanted anything made, from a palace to a pair of golden shoes, they went down to Hephaestus, where he worked in his shop underneath Mount Etna.

It is said that Hephaestus once displeased his father, Zeus, so that Zeus threw him from Mount Olympus. He fell for an entire day, and he was so **injured** by his fall that he was always **lame** afterward. Still he was very wise, and the gods liked him for the beautiful things he made for them.

As Phoebus Apollo was god of the sun, Artemis was the goddess of the moon. These two were brother and sister. They furnished nearly all the light that men had by day or night.

....

banquets feasts
injured hurt
lame not able to walk well or without pain

Artemis was tall and strong and swift, and she was as good a hunter as her twin brother, Apollo. In fact, she was also the goddess of hunting.

Ares was the cruel god of war. He **rejoiced** in the noise and blood of battle. Wherever he went, **destruction** followed.

Aphrodite was the goddess of love and beauty. She was the most beautiful of all the goddesses, and Zeus's favorite daughter. No one could look upon her without loving her.

Aphrodite had a son, Eros, a **rascal** who had a bow and arrow that he used to **torment** both gods and men. Whoever was struck by one of his arrows was sure to fall in love with the next person he met. As Eros was not at all careful whom he wounded, or when or where, he caused a great deal of trouble.

rejoiced took pleasure from something
destruction ruin
rascal a troublemaker
torment to bother greatly

Hermes, another son of Zeus, was Zeus's messenger. He wore wings on his hat and on his sandals. Whenever Zeus wished to send news to the earth, Hermes would fly down faster than you can imagine. He invented the lyre upon which Phoebus Apollo played, and gave it to him as a present.

These gods, and sometimes others, used to meet in the banquet hall of Zeus and talk over their own affairs and the affairs of men. The food they ate was called ambrosia, and the drink, nectar—food and drink for the gods alone.

These banquets were not always pleasant, for the gods did not always agree. Sometimes they had very bitter and very foolish **quarrels**, as when three of the goddesses quarreled over which of them was the fairest.

Zeus had two brothers who did not live on Mount Olympus, though they were great gods. Their names were Poseidon and Hades.

Poseidon was the ruler of the sea. He could make the oceans calm and quiet, or stir up giant, crashing waves.

Hades ruled the underworld, the dark regions underneath the earth where, the Greeks believed, people went when they died.

quarrels arguments

About the Names of Greek and Roman Gods

After the Greeks, another great people rose to power. These people, the Romans, lived in the land we now call Italy. The Romans borrowed many ideas and **customs** from the Greeks, including their religion. The Romans **worshipped** the same gods as the Greeks but called them by different names, as shown in the table at right. When you read myths in this and other books, you will sometimes see the Greek names, and sometimes the Roman.

----

customs traditions; ways of life
worshipped prayed or honored

Names of Greek and Roman Gods

GREEK NAME	ROMAN NAME	
Zeus	Jupiter	king of the gods
Hera	Juno	wife of Zeus, queen of the gods
Athena	Minerva	goddess of wisdom
Aphrodite	Venus	goddess of love and beauty
Eros	Cupid	god of love, son of Aphrodite
Ares	Mars	god of war
Artemis	Diana	goddess of the moon and hunting
Demeter	Ceres	goddess of corn and growing things
Hephaestus	Vulcan	god of fire and the forge
Hermes	Mercury	the messenger god
Persephone	Proserpina	daughter of Demeter
Apollo*	Apollo*	god of the sun, music, and poetry
Poseidon	Neptune	god of the sea
Hades	Pluto	god of the underworld

* Apollo is sometimes called Phoebus Apollo.

The *Naming of a* Great City

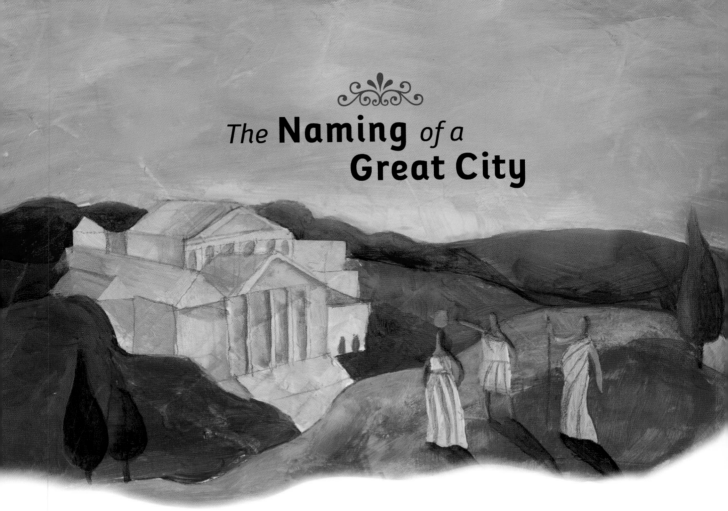

Long ago, the people of a far country built a beautiful city. It stood on a high hill overlooking the blue sea. The people laid out the streets with care and crowned the hill with beautiful buildings. The city was very **fair** to look upon.

"What shall we call our beautiful city?" said the people.

"Name it for me," said Poseidon, the great god of the sea. "I will make your city stronger than any other city on the earth."

....

fair pleasant to look at; lovely

"**Nay**, call it for me," said Athena, the goddess of wisdom. "The gifts that I can give you are worth far more than any gift of strength."

The people of the city did not know how to choose between Poseidon and Athena. "We are only people of the earth," they said. "How can we decide between the gods?"

So they called to Zeus, the king of the gods: "Great Zeus, tell us what to do. For whom shall we name our beautiful city on the hill?"

Zeus answered, "Both Athena and Poseidon offer you good gifts. Let them bring you their gifts. The one who brings the better gift may claim the city. I myself will be the judge."

nay no

When the day of the contest came, all the people of the city gathered together. Zeus then told the god of the sea to bring forth his gift.

Poseidon appeared, leading by the bridle a shining warhorse, strong, **swift**, and harnessed for battle.

"I offer you war, glory, and power," he said, and the people of the city cheered loud and long.

Now it was Athena's turn. She came forward quietly, carrying something in her hand. Kneeling before the people, she dug a hole in the ground and placed in it a tiny seed.

A leaf appeared, then a stalk, and then a tree, covered with glossy green leaves and **laden** with fruit. It was an olive tree.

Athena turned and faced the people. "In this tree is life, peace, and plenty," she said.

The people stood in silence, waiting for the great judge to speak.

Then said Zeus, "Athena brings the better gift. The city shall be called Athens."

With one voice, the people took up the cry, "Athens! Athens! The city shall be named for Athena. She has given us the greater gift!" ⌇

swift fast
laden heavily loaded

The *Greater* Gift

Characters

KING

POSEIDON

ATHENA

ZEUS

TOWNSPEOPLE

Time

ANCIENT TIMES

Place

A BEAUTIFUL CITY ON A HIGH HILL BY THE SEA IN GREECE

Scene 1

A SUMMER AFTERNOON

*King enters, **strolling** slowly across the stage, stopping at center.*

KING: What a glorious day! And what a glorious city! Our temples glow like pearls. The red and orange roofs of our houses gleam like rubies. And our trees and fields glitter like emeralds from here to the golden beach and the **sapphire** sea.

....

strolling walking without hurrying
sapphire a clear stone, usually dark blue

Our beautiful city crowns this hill. This hill crowns the land. This land crowns all the other lands in all the world. Truly, there is no better place to live than this city.

Poseidon and Athena enter.

Good day to you, strangers, and welcome.

POSEIDON *(gruffly)*: Good day to you, King. My friend and I have been **admiring** your **fair** city. Tell me, what is the name of this place?

KING: Ah, noble sir, our city does not yet have a name.

POSEIDON: Why not?

KING: The people have met many times, but we can think of no name great enough for our **marvelous** city.

POSEIDON: Then name the city after me: Poseidon!

KING *(surprised)*: Poseidon! The mighty god of the sea!

POSEIDON: Yes—and if you name this city after me, I will give your city a gift that will make it stronger than any other city on the earth.

ATHENA: No, good king, call the city for me. I am Athena, goddess of wisdom. I can give you a gift worth far more than any gift of strength.

KING: Thanks to you both. But how shall we decide between so mighty a god and so wise a goddess? We are only people of the earth. We cannot decide

---

admiring praising
fair pleasant to look at; lovely
marvelous wonderful

between the gods. We must turn to Zeus, the king of the gods. Only he can decide for whom we shall name our beautiful city on the hill.

ZEUS *(from offstage)*: Good king, both Athena and Poseidon offer you great gifts. Let them bring their gifts for all to see. The one who brings the better gift may claim the city. I myself will be the judge.

SCENE 2

A FEW DAYS LATER

Athena and Poseidon stand on one side of the stage. King and Townspeople stand on the other. Zeus enters.

ZEUS: Poseidon, bring forth your gift.

POSEIDON: Very well. See my power!

Poseidon strikes the ground with his trident. A white horse runs onto the stage.

This is my gift. His name is Horse. Horse will carry your **burdens**, pull your chariots, and let you sit on his back while he runs as fast as the wind. He and his kind will bring you glory in war and power over your enemies.

TOWNSPEOPLE *(clapping and cheering)*: Poseidon and power! Hurrah!

....

burdens loads of heavy things

ZEUS: Enough! Athena, bring forth your gift.

Athena steps forward. She carries a pot with a small tree in it.

TOWNSPEOPLE: A leaf? A stalk? Is this all that Athena brings?

ATHENA: From this small stalk will grow a tree. And from its fruit will grow many more trees that will **thrive** even in this rocky land. These trees will give you food when you are hungry. They will give you shade when you are hot. They will add to your city's beauty, and people all over the world will use the oil from the fruit. I give you the olive tree. In this tree is life, peace, and plenty.

Townspeople are silent. They look at Zeus.

ZEUS: Athena brings the greater gift. The city shall be called Athens.

TOWNSPEOPLE AND KING: Athens! Athens! The city shall be named for Athena. She has given us the greater gift! ꙮ

---

thrive to grow well and easily

The *Story* *of* **Arachne**

In the city of Athens in the days of long ago, there lived a **maiden** named Arachne.

Arachne was skilled in the art of spinning and weaving. Not one of the maidens of Athens could spin such fine thread or weave such wonderful cloth as she could.

As time went on, Arachne grew **vain** and proud. "I am the most wonderful spinner and weaver in the world," she said.

"Next to our great goddess Athena," added the good people of Athens.

"**Nay**," said Arachne boldly, "I do not fear even Athena's skill and power. I know that I can spin and weave as well as she."

---

maiden a young girl
vain showing too much pride; thinking highly of oneself
nay no

"Take care," said the wise people of Athens. "Take care, for your **boasting** may anger Athena."

Still Arachne did not **heed** their warning. She grew more vain and boasted more and more. At last the goddess took notice of her foolish boasting.

One day as Arachne was working at her loom, an old woman appeared before her.

"My dear," said the stranger, "you boast that you are as skillful as Athena. Try your skill with the maidens, but do not **strive** with the goddess."

"I am not afraid of Athena," said the maiden. "Let her try her skill with me if she dares."

Then the stranger threw back her dark cloak and showed herself—the beautiful, golden-haired, gray-eyed Athena. "I am ready," she said.

boasting bragging
heed listen; obey
strive to try very hard; to struggle

The other maidens were frightened. Only Arachne was not afraid. "Let us begin," she said.

"First, hear this," said Athena. "If your cloth is best, I will weave no more. But if mine is best, you will never weave again. Do you agree?"

"I agree," said Arachne.

Then the people of Athens looked on in wonder as the goddess and the maiden worked at their looms.

Athena wove into her cloth pictures of the great gods—Zeus and Hera, Apollo and Poseidon, and all the others. No one had ever seen anything as wonderful as her pictures.

Arachne had great skill, but the pictures that she wove were not noble and beautiful like Athena's. They showed her own proud spirit.

As soon as her cloth was finished, Arachne looked at the other cloth. She knew that it was much more beautiful than hers. She was filled with **grief** and anger. "If I can never weave again, how can I live? All my joy in life is gone. Let me die."

"Nay," said Athena, "you shall not die. You shall go on spinning and weaving forever." And with a touch, she turned Arachne into the first spider, which ran to a corner and quickly wove a beautiful, shining web.

"You and your kind," said Athena, "shall always be the greatest spinners and weavers on the earth."

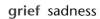

grief sadness

The *Story of* Proserpina

An old myth tells us of a king whose name was Pluto, and whose home was deep down in the earth where the rays of the sun never shine.

In all the **realms** of this king, there was no joy of life, no light of day. His was a world of grief, tears, and the shades of night. And so, at times he came up to the land of love and hope and joy to find, if he could, something that would cheer his sad life and make it less full of **woe**.

---

realms kingdoms
woe great sadness

One day, when the fields were bright with blooms, King Pluto thought that he would ride out and see some of the **fair** things that had been born of the earth and sun. To see these things, he hoped, might touch a spring of joy in his sad heart.

He rode up by way of Mount Etna, and out through the clouds of steam that pour from its top. Then, with a sharp word to his steeds, he drove in great haste down the **steep** slopes and did not stop till he reached the green fields at their base.

fair pleasant to look at; lovely
steep at a very sharp angle

Poor Proserpina screamed and tried to leap from the chariot, but the stern, sad king **soothed** her fears with kind words and told her that so long as she would stay with him, she should be free from harm. Then a sheet of flame shot up and shut out the light of day. The steeds, the chariot, the king, and the maid went down, down, down, and were seen no more.

When news was brought to good Ceres that her child was lost, she did not faint or cry out in her great grief, for she was too brave and wise to do that. But she went out at once in search of her child, and she **vowed** that she would find her or come back no more.

With a black veil wound around her head, and with a torch in her hand, she crossed the seas and went from land to land, and asked all that **dwelt** on the earth if

soothed calmed or quieted
vowed promised
dwelt lived

they had seen her child. For a whole year, she searched in vain. Then she thought that she would ask Helios, who drives the chariot of the sun through the skies.

"Great Helios," she said, "I know that your eye takes in the whole world, and that all the deeds of men are known to you. Tell me, I pray you, have you seen my lost child, Proserpina?"

Kind Helios was glad that Ceres had come to him. Yes, he had seen Proserpina. He had seen Pluto rush down from Etna, and had seen him lift the child from the ground into his black chariot. He had seen the wild leap down Mount Etna's throat.

"The maid is in Pluto's dark realms," he said, "and Pluto has made her his queen. But he would not have seized her as he did without permission from Jupiter, the king of earth and air."

Then Ceres gave way to grief and rage. She sent word to Jupiter that no fruits or grain should grow in all the world while Pluto kept Proserpina in his dark home. For it was Ceres, men said, who gave life to the trees and plants and made them bloom and bear fruit.

Jupiter and the great ones who were with him knew that Ceres would be true to her word, and the thought filled them with fear. If there should be no fruit or grains for men, and no food for them but fish and flesh, they would soon be as wild as in the old, old times, and there would be no good deeds done in all the world.

"The best thing that we can do," said Jupiter, "is to bring Proserpina back."

So he ordered Mercury, who had winged feet, to go down to the halls of Pluto and fetch the lost maid back.

Pluto was glad to see Mercury, but he frowned when he learned why Mercury had come.

"Do you know the law?" he asked.

"What law?" said Mercury.

"There is a law that no one can break," said Pluto. "I will read it to you."

Then he took a black book from a shelf on the wall, and read these words: "That one, be it god or man, maid or child, who tastes food while in the land of Pluto, shall not go **thence** so long as the world stands."

....

thence an old-fashioned way of saying "from that place"

Then Mercury asked Proserpina if food had passed her lips since the day that she had come to Pluto's land. She told him that she had been too sad to think of food. Yet once she had **plucked** some bright red fruit that grew on a tree by the banks of the dark stream that people call the Styx.

"Did you taste it?"

"Yes, I took one small bite, and then threw the rest far from me."

King Pluto laughed loud and long. But Mercury asked him, "What kind of bright red fruit grows on the banks of the dark stream that you call the Styx?"

"**Pomegranates**," said the king.

"Is a pomegranate food?" asked Mercury. "At the best, not more than one-third of it is fit to eat. The rest is skin and seeds."

plucked picked
pomegranates red fruits that are full of small, tart seeds

Then he took Proserpina back to the bright earth. Ceres stood at the door of the great cave, and Mercury placed her dear child in her arms. Then he told her that, for two-thirds of each year, Proserpina might stay with her and make her and all the world glad. But he said that, for the rest of the time, she must go back to Pluto's dark realms.

And so it is that when Proserpina stays in the dark lands of Pluto, the days grow chill with frost and snow, and the grains of corn lie dead in the ground. But when the sad-faced king brings her back, the days grow bright and warm. Then Ceres is happy, and the stalks begin to grow and the buds of the fruit trees burst forth.

A **Flight Through** *the* **Sky**

Long ago on a faraway island, there lived a man named Daedalus.

Daedalus was famed throughout the land for his skill with his hands. No other man of his time was so clever in building. His mind was always full of plans to make something new.

But though he was held in great honor, Daedalus was really a prisoner. The cruel king of the island knew how skillful he was and would not let him go away.

As time went on, Daedalus grew **weary** of his life on the island and wished to escape. But it was impossible for him to get away by sea. On every side, the king's strong ships kept watch.

For a long time, Daedalus wondered how he could escape. At last he hit upon a daring plan.

"The king may control the land and sea," he said, "but he does not control the air. I will go that way."

No man had ever before tried to do what he planned to do. He planned to make two sets of wings, one for himself and one for his young son Icarus, so that they could fly away.

weary very tired

He set to work secretly collecting feathers, small ones and large ones. Then he made a light frame of wood, with cloth stretched over it. Very carefully he laid the feathers all over the frame, and held them firmly in place with wax.

Night after night he worked in secret, until at last he had finished a pair of wings. As soon as these were ready, he strapped them on his son's shoulders. He showed the boy how to flap them like a bird, and slowly young Icarus learned to fly.

Each night Daedalus secretly worked on the second pair of wings, and each night Icarus tried his skill at flying.

At last all was ready. Early in the morning, Daedalus and his son stole down to the beach, carrying their wings.

As the father strapped the boy's wings in place, he said, "Icarus, my son, listen to what I say. Be sure to keep the middle track. If you fly too low over the sea, your wings will get wet. If you go too high, the heat of the sun will melt the wax on your wings. Be very careful. Do not fly too close to the sun."

Icarus promised, eager to be off. Then as Daedalus gave the word, they raised their wings and rose up, up over the sea like great birds.

The morning sun shone on their feathers so that they **glistened** like gold. The cool air from the ocean touched their faces. A great thrill went through the boy as he felt himself soaring up through the morning air.

He forgot his father's warning. He swooped down to the waves, and then rose again higher and higher into the sky.

Suddenly, before he could stop himself, he had flown too near the hot sun. The burning heat melted the wax. The feathers loosened and fell in a soft shower into the water.

In vain Icarus flapped his arms. His wings were now useless. Down he dropped—down, down to the sea.

"Icarus," cried his father. "Icarus, where are you?" No answer came. Only the feathers floating on the water showed him what had happened.

Poor Daedalus flew on till he came safely to land. But he was so sad at the loss of his son that he never used his wings again.

---

glistened shined or gleamed
in vain without success